A Guide to the Methodist Art Collection

By Roger Wollen

with additional contributions by Miriam Davies,
John N Gibbs and Sarah Middleton
Including a Foreword by Richard Cork
and an Introduction by Graham Kent

Published by the Trustees of the Methodist Church
Collection of Modern Christian Art 2010

This is an expanded and revised edition of a publication
first produced in 2000 under the title 'The Methodist
Church Collection of Modern Christian Art: An Introduction'
and reprinted in 2004. With minor changes, the entries on
artists whose work was present in the Collection by 2000
are reduced versions of those which appear in 'Catalogue
of the Methodist Church Collection of Modern Christian
Art' by Roger Wollen. This was published by the Trustees
of the Collection in 2003 (ISBN 0-9538135-1-7, 178pp.).
Entries on artists whose work has been acquired since
2000 are written by the Trustees. The Introduction is
written by Graham Kent. The Trustees are very grateful to
Richard Cork for his Foreword.

© RW appears after the entries written by Roger Wollen.
© T after the remainder

© photographs the Trustees of the Methodist Collection
of Modern Christian Art

Design by Stephen Lambert of the Methodist
Connexional Team

Printed by G.W.Chapman & Sons Print Limited, Middlesex

ISBN 0-9538135-2-5

For information on borrowing the Methodist Collection
and on the programme of exhibitions, please visit
www.methodist.org.uk/artcollection

Foreword

Looking back over my career as an art critic, I realise that the admirable Methodist Collection formed the subject of my very first published review. It was commissioned in May 1964 by Broadside, an adventurous magazine produced by boys at Kingswood School. At the age of seventeen, I was already fascinated by art history and the compulsive urge to make my own paintings, drawings and sculpture. So I enjoyed writing about *The Church And The Artist Exhibition* when it arrived at Kingswood, and began by declaring that the Methodist Collection "clearly demands a consideration of the place of religion in art. Are any worthwhile painters today Christian? How too can religious themes be expressed in our prevailing abstract idioms? Many artists would claim with Mondrian that it is not the business of art to express ideas and sentiments which are essentially literary; or if they are religious, the paintings should be general statements of a mystic character."

In the end, though, the exhibits which triggered my most intense admiration were figurative rather than abstract. I decided that "Burra's *Pool of Bethesda* with its overpowering forms, rich sombre colours and horrible searchlights was exciting, if a rather puzzling interpretation of its subject, and in the same way Souza's *Crucifixion* compels respect by its brutal distortion, the obvious driving sincerity behind it, and the superbly electric blue of the sky."

Ultimately, the artist who won me over with the greatest profundity was a Frenchman. "Above all," I wrote in my final paragraph, "there were the two Rouault aquatints, in which the limitations of the medium were perfectly suited to express the tragic compassion of the artist's vision… We feel in front of these Rouaults an awe which is surely the test of all great painting; indeed, all great art is essentially an act of faith, Christian or otherwise."

Although several decades have passed since I penned those words as a teenager at Kingswood, I still completely agree with that concluding sentence. And I am now delighted to pay tribute to the stimulating role played by the Methodist Collection at a crucial stage in my life, helping me realise just how much I relished the challenge of writing about art.

© ***Richard Cork***

Richard Cork is an award-winning art critic, historian, broadcaster and exhibition curator. His many books include Vorticism (1976), Art Beyond The Gallery (1985), David Bomberg (1987), A Bitter Truth: Avant-Garde Art and the Great War (1995), four acclaimed volumes of his critical writings on modern art (2003), and Wild Thing: Epstein, Gaudier-Brzeska, Gill (2009).

Contents

Introduction

'God saw all that He had made and it was very good'

(Genesis 1 v 31)

'Christ is the image of the invisible God, His is the primacy over all creation. Everything is created … in Him and for Him, all things are held together in Him'

(Colossians 1 v15f)

'We are God's work of art, created for the life … which God has designed for us'

(Ephesians 2 v10)

Alongside these Biblical texts is the fact that Bezalel, the first named person to receive the Holy Spirit was an artist, designer and organiser of other people's skills (Exodus 31 and related chapters). He can, perhaps, be seen to be part of a travelling art project where the quality of what was made created a faithful community, enhanced worship and gave praise to God.

The Methodist Church has found itself with an amazing art collection thanks to the foresight, energy and generosity of two people. There is no precise way of measuring its impact on individuals, or on worship and teaching but I know from arranging the tours over the last twenty years, what a profound effect it can have.

The Collection is shown, in whole or in part, in chapels, churches and cathedrals, in museums and galleries, and in schools, colleges and universities. It is used in devotional settings and in larger gatherings. It has prompted churches to work with the visual arts as part of their mission strategy and to improve the visual impact of their premises.

The life of the Collection grows from a theology arising from the texts quoted above and finds its place within the wider purposes of the Methodist church. It is exciting to work with others to use the Collection - whether in an arts festival, a mission event, or an educational project - or all three together! And it is equally exciting to see how people respond to the individual works - whether it be to the choice of colour, the artistic quality or the subject matter. The Collection drives us to think about what Christ means to us and to look again at the Bible story: this has been the role of the visual arts as part of the language of the Church for most of its history.

The World Council of Churches headquarters in Geneva and the Vatican Galleries also have contemporary art collections and they face the same question as the Trustees of the Collection: How does one keep a Collection like this open and alive? The answer is that the Collection must continue to grow!

What acquisitions do we then make? There are gaps in our narrative of Christ's life story, there are artists and artistic movements we would like to see represented and there are certain styles and materials that are lacking. As this booklet shows, we have made some progress. Thus several of our recent acquisitions reflect the fact that we are a multi-racial denomination and are part of a worldwide church. We have also increased the proportion of work by women artists. In some cases we have bought from galleries but in others we have gone direct to the artist or commissioned the artist to tackle a particular subject. To support this programme, we have benefited from our general fund-raising and from some benefactions. We would like to continue in what is an exciting and privileged ministry. Today there are more artists dealing with Christian and religious themes and there is a greater interest in spirituality than was the case 30 or 40 years ago. Even if only to a small extent, this may be fruit from seed which this Collection has sown.

© *Graham Kent*

The Revd Graham Kent is Secretary of the Trustees of the Collection and holds a Masters Degree in Art History. He is currently Ecumenical Officer for Greater Manchester Churches Together.

The History of the Methodist Church Collection of Modern Christian Art

The Methodist Church's Collection of modern Christian art was created over forty years ago, although there have been a number of subsequent additions to it. It was the initiative, in the early 1960s, of a Methodist layman, Dr John Morel Gibbs, who believed that the quality of 'religious art' and 'church furnishings' was poor, and hoped that an extensively exhibited Collection would help draw attention to the situation and encourage a more imaginative approach to the commissioning and buying of paintings, sculpture and church furnishings.

It so happened that he knew the Rev. Douglas Wollen, who had been the minister of one of the two Methodist churches in his home town of Penarth, just outside Cardiff. Aware of his interest in the visual arts, and the fact that he wrote regularly on art exhibitions and Collections for The Times and other periodicals, John Gibbs invited Douglas Wollen to create a Collection of contemporary religious works of art and gave him a largely free hand to decide the nature of the Collection and the artists and works to be included.

Starting work in 1962, Douglas Wollen visited London galleries, contacted a range of artists whose work he knew and felt might be appropriate and visited a great many exhibitions, mostly in London but also in other parts of the country. Some purchases were made on what he described as his 'Bond Street Crawl' when he was in London for Methodist meetings, others were made direct from artists. One work was commissioned and one was bought at auction.

In addition to creating the Collection, Douglas Wollen organized a tour that, by today's standards, would be inconceivable. Under the title 'The Church and the Artist', the Collection toured between July 1963 and September 1965 from Plymouth to Newcastle upon Tyne, from London to Preston and from Penarth to Bedford. It was shown at major art galleries such as the Walker in Liverpool, the Birmingham and Manchester City galleries, the Graves at Sheffield and the National Museum of Wales (at its out-station, the Turner House, in Penarth). In the East Midlands the exhibition was toured by the Area Museums Council; elsewhere Douglas Wollen arranged the showings and the Methodist Education Committee handled the physical arrangements with transport provided by another Methodist layman, Pat Welch, whose business in Birmingham had suitable vehicles.

The paintings and reliefs were accompanied by a subsidiary exhibition on church design and furnishings which relied largely on photographs and design drawings but included some original art and craft work. In most cases this exhibition was shown at the same venue as the paintings and reliefs but was sometimes at a Methodist church, a college or design centre. The exhibitions were generally well received, with attendances of well over 107,000 at the thirty venues. After the tour finished the intention was that the Collection (then formally the responsibility of the Methodist Education Committee) should be housed indefinitely at Kingswood School in Bath, a Methodist school which had suitable facilities. However, after a few years the works were lent individually, or in groups of two or three, to Methodist schools and colleges around the country. One episode during these years merits description. This involved Graham Sutherland's painting The Deposition, which had been hung in the assembly hall at Hunmanby Hall in Yorkshire. One girl became obsessed by it, and eventually, unable to restrain herself and feeling that some of her fellow pupils did not value it enough, she took it with her when she left for the end-of-term holidays. The school did not note the loss, but the girl talked to her sister when she reached home, and the picture (which had been removed from its frame) was returned anonymously, rolled up and wrapped in brown paper. It was sent, at Sutherland's suggestion, to Marlborough Fine Art in London for restoration and re-framing. While it was there he called and seeing the painting, commented that he remembered painting it. Noticing that it was not signed, he signed it there and then. The pupil who had caused all the trouble came back to the school after medical treatment and the painting was returned and re-hung!

In 1978 it was felt that the condition and circumstances in which several of the works were kept left something to be desired, and it was decided to bring them together again at Southlands College of Education. Initially, Southlands was a suitable venue with an active art department and a chaplain, the Rev. Jim Bates, who was keen to use the Collection in his teaching and in other ways. Over the years, however, there were major changes in the staff and status of the College, and interest in the pictures declined.

In 1990, John Gibbs took the initiative to show the Collection as part of a Festival of Christian Art in Penarth. For this, the works were 'rescued' from Southlands by Tim Egan, then the Registrar of the National Museum and Gallery of Wales. A considerable amount of restoration work was undertaken, as four pictures had been damaged in a flood, and then, together with some of the National Museum's own pictures, notably four by David Jones, the Collection was hung at the Turner House, at that time an outstation of the National Museum .

The decision was then taken by the Methodist Church's Division of Education and Youth (which had taken over from the old Education Committee and, as a result, had acquired the custodianship of the works), to bring the Collection to the DEY offices at Muswell Hill in north London. News of its availability for display quickly spread and over the next seven years the Collection was exhibited at a wide variety of venues. In 1998 it acquired a new base when it was placed on loan at Westminster College, Oxford. At the same time a body of Trustees was formed, charged with caring for and promoting the Collection. The Chairman was Dr John Newton Gibbs, eldest son of John Morel Gibbs, and the Secretary was the Rev Graham Kent. The loan programme was further developed with many successful exhibitions, the majority of them being ecumenical in nature. A significant change came in 2001 when Westminster College merged with Oxford Brookes University. Care of the Collection was safe-guarded under a legal agreement between the University and Westminster College Oxford Trust Ltd. In addition to organising the exhibition programme, the Trustees have drawn up an acquisitions policy and guided by this have acquired a number of new works. An Annual Report is produced and a Friends Group has been formed.

© *RW*

Notes

rc = Roman Catholic   RCA = Royal College of Art
Bible extracts in the main body of the text are from the New Revised Standard Version.
All measurements are in the form 'height by width'.
'Selected Collections' only comprise UK Collections
Unattributed quotations from the artists have been taken from correspondence and conversations with the authors.

The works in the Collection

Norman Adams

Born: Walthamstow 1927

Studied: Harrow School of Art 1940–6; RCA, London 1948–51

Selected commissions: murals at St Anselms, Kennington, London 1971; Stations of the Cross, Our Lady of Lourdes, Milton Keynes 1975

Selected collections: Tate Gallery, London; Victoria and Albert Museum, London; Scottish National Gallery of Modern Art, Edinburgh; Ashmolean Museum, Oxford; Birmingham City Museums and Art Gallery; Leeds University Collection; Manchester City Art Gallery; Whitworth Art Gallery, Manchester.

1 Christ's entry into Jerusalem

Watercolour on paper, 1991. 83 cm by 97 cm. Signed and inscribed bottom right, 'Christ's entry into Jerusalem'.

The next day the great crowd that had come to the festival heard that Jesus was coming to Jerusalem. So they took branches of palm trees and went out to meet him shouting, 'Hosanna! Blessed is the one who comes in the name of the Lord – the King of Israel!'

Jesus found a young donkey and sat on it, as it is written: 'Do not be afraid, daughter of Zion. Look, your king is coming, sitting on a donkey's colt!'

(John 12: 12–15)

The painting shows Jesus riding left to right upon a donkey accompanied by a foal, or colt, entering not so much Jerusalem as an unspecified city (with a number of flags visible – the Union Jack, the flag of St George, the German flag – these latter two flown on their side and upside down respectively – and what appears to be the Swedish flag). There is no evidence of palm-tree branches or garments cast in front of Jesus (although there are prominent sunflowers lining the route) but there is a joyous crowd (of adults, children and animals) and much bunting and decoration. An unidentified disciple greets Jesus and three dark cloaked figures proceed him. The figure shown to the right, at a window, may be

1

Zacchaeus, a rich man, who, being small, couldn't see Jesus. So he ran ahead and climbed a tree. In this urban setting a window rather than a tree makes a good vantage point. The incident is reported by Luke as happening at Jericho, but it is not uncommon for it to be included in the Entry into Jerusalem. The picture is clearly influenced by James Ensor's Christ's entry into Brussels, which Adams has identified as one of his favourite paintings.

Colour has always played a major part in Adams' work (although the subject, often a 'moralistic' one, has always been equally important to him) and the colour in his watercolours and oils is much more than a surface sensation in which we can revel. As Peter Fuller said in his introduction to the catalogue of the 'Colour Chart of a Way' exhibition (1988), there is a strong element of medieval stained glass in these works, a richness and luminosity, a recognition that colour

is an inescapable element in life and in religion, something in which we should glory. Fuller also places Adams in the great British romantic tradition with Ruskin and Blake, a tradition that also took full advantage of the wealth of colour that is found in nature, nature being the preferred subject matter for art and the preferred route to God.

For Adams there is a rich seam of creative ambiguity between nature and religion, the sensuous and the spiritual and the pagan and the Christian. 'I can trace everything I have done back to a source of inspiration in nature. More or less everything was conceived in direct communication with nature.' At the same time, his involvement with nature has fed directly into his interest in religion. He once remarked that 'nature is marked all over with crucifixes' – for example, the form of the cross is discernible on various leaves and grasses.

The painting was commissioned

for the Methodist Collection in 1990. When asked to undertake the work Adams replied that he 'would like to do this very much … It is a wonderful subject', and he couldn't think why he had not painted it before.

Ralph Beyer

Born: Berlin, Germany 1921
Died: London 2008

Studied: apprentice/assistant to Eric Gill 1937; Central School of Art and Design (then Art and Crafts), London 1938–9; Chelsea School of Art (Henry Moore's sculpture classes)

Selected commissions: altar inscription and carvings, Foundation of St Katherine, Butcher Row, London 1954; Tablets of the Word and other works, Coventry Cathedral 1956–63; foundation stone, incised crosses on altar, twelve consecration stones and inscriptions on three panels (exterior of porch), St Paul's Church, Bow Common, London; work at Paul Tillich Memorial Park, New Harmony, Indiana, USA; inscription for Edith Sitwell memorial, Weedon Lois, Northamptonshire (sculpture by Henry Moore) 1967–8; Noel Coward memorial, Westminster Abbey 1983–4

Selected collections: RCA London; Victoria and Albert Museum, London

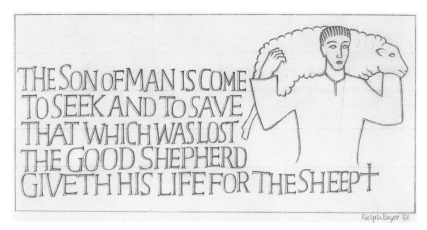

THE SON OF MAN IS COME TO SEEK AND TO SAVE THAT WHICH WAS LOST THE GOOD SHEPHERD GIVETH HIS LIFE FOR THE SHEEP✝

Ralph Beyer '61

2

2 The son of man is come

Pencil, 1961, 20 cm by 38 cm. Signed and dated bottom right.

This is a study for one of the Tablets of the Word at Coventry Cathedral which the cathedral's architect, Sir Basil Spence, commissioned from Ralph Beyer. The full text, which is taken from Luke 19: 10 and John 10: 11, reads: 'For the Son of Man came to seek out and to save the lost. The good shepherd lays down his life for the sheep.' To the right of the text, which is written in capital letters, is a figure of the good shepherd carrying a sheep upon his shoulders. The portrayal of Christ as the Good Shepherd who looks after his flock (of Christians) is based partly upon two parables in the New Testament (Luke 15: 3–7 and John 10: 1–18), partly upon Psalm 23 ('The Lord is My Shepherd') and passages in Isaiah (40: 11) and Ezekiel (34: 2–31). Luke is the source of the portrayal of Jesus with the sheep across his shoulders: 'Which one of you, having a hundred sheep, and losing one of them, does not leave the ninety-nine in the wilderness, and go after the one that is lost, until he finds it? When he has found it, he lays it on his shoulders and rejoices.'

The Tablets of the Word are eight large stone blocks (4.5 m by 1.8 m) carrying carved texts and symbols placed around the nave walls of the new Coventry Cathedral. The drawing is dated 1961 and Coventry Cathedral was consecrated in 1962.

Ralph Beyer came to England as a refugee from Nazi Germany in 1937. He initially joined Eric Gill as an apprentice at Pigotts in Buckinghamshire but quickly left to study sculpture. He subsequently worked with David Kindersley and the Cambridge firm of Rattee and Kett before embarking on a freelance, and later teaching, career as a sculptor and letterer.

Beyer persuaded Spence and the Cathedral authorities to accept texts in freely composed lettering, with no two letters being identical. Some of the symbols, including that of the Good Shepherd, already existed but the others were created by Beyer. 'The Good Shepherd', with the sheep on the shepherd's shoulders, is found in early Christian sculpture (both free-standing and as decoration in relief on sarcophagi) and in inscriptions, particularly in the Roman catacombs, which also had a profound influence on the style of lettering adopted by Beyer.

This design for Coventry was not part of the original collection but was included in the subsidiary exhibition devoted to church furnishings and design. In 1990 the decision was taken to add it to the main collection.

© *RW*

John Brokenshire

Born: Gloucestershire 1958

Studied: Fine Art, Sheffield Hallam University

Selected collections: B.P. International Ltd, London; Babcock & Brown London; Watershed Northampton; Aviva Insurance London; Computer Science Corporation, Farnborough

3 Untitled – Pentecost

Oil on canvas, 2003, 76cm x 77 cm.

See entry number 15 for Biblical text

This abstract painting is perhaps best described by the artist himself 'The work was a long time in the making. Its final form came together as a synthesis of various key concerns I had been living with and pondering. First it came from a period of interest in shadow and light as pictorial elements and the desire to create paintings from their interaction. Meanwhile the white floating image was thanks to drawings I had been making in the museum from stuffed birds. Over time I began to visit snowy owls and wrens in my imagination and they became emblems of purity and grace. I was keen to get a very loosely represented image of a bird in space into my painting. But I wanted a sense of a bird hovering, not on a trajectory. At the same time I hoped to refer in some way to angels: even if very obliquely by colour alone or by suggestion. Darkness had to be the counterpoint to this. I had been looking at the depth of shade found in Rembrandt and Caravaggio. In such paintings enormous stillness and drama can co-exist. I had been pondering how to convey a sense of a powerful, compelling moment that can be so vivid within figurative art. When the painting came together it felt as if these elements had meshed.

For many years my painting had been an effort to create my own vocabulary and to honour the natural world. A longstanding hope has been to convey a sense of the mystery within nature. But recently I have felt a shift and a longing to refer more openly to the inner world. I would define inner space not as a space of sanctuary, but of involvement, journey, even encounter. There is more of a sense of urgency or pressure to deal with new material, related to transformation and the awareness of spiritual help and guidance. The title Pentecost was not suggested by me, but was the highest interpretation I could hope for from any viewer. I have long believed in God: I was first drawn to the spiritual in nature and in the practice of meditation and in my reading. I have been fortunate to take part in healing circles and then have strongly felt a sense of a wonderful benign force. I would search to re-encounter this presence, and would even hope to find it in the process of painting. Gently and gradually I made my way back to the church. I was concerned about the spiritual needs of my young children. Now I wish it had been much sooner!'

© *T*

Edward Burra

Born: London 1905 **Died:** 1976

Studied: Chelsea Polytechnic, London 1921–3; RCA, London 1923–5

Selected collections: British Museum, London; Tate Gallery, London; Victoria and Albert Museum, London; Scottish National Gallery of Modern Art, Edinburgh

3

4 The pool of Bethesda
Watercolour, 1951–2,
110 cm by 152 cm.

Now in Jerusalem by the Sheep Gate there is a pool, called in Hebrew Bethesda, which has five porticos. In these lay many invalids blind, lame, and paralysed. (Some manuscripts add: They were waiting for the water to move, because every now and then an angel of the Lord went down into the pool and stirred up the water. The first sick person to go into the pool after

4

the water was stirred up was healed from whatever disease he had.) One man was there who had been ill for thirty-eight years. When Jesus saw him lying there and knew that he had been there a long time, he said to him, 'Do you want to be made well?' The sick man answered him, 'Sir, I have no one to put me into the pool when the water is stirred up; and while I am making my way, someone else steps down ahead of me.' Jesus said to him, 'Stand up, take your mat and walk.' At once the man was made well, and he took up his mat and began to walk.

Now that day was a sabbath. So the Jews said to the man who had been cured, 'It is the sabbath; it is not lawful for you to carry your mat.' But he answered them, 'The man who made me well said to me, "Take up your mat and walk." They asked him, 'Who is the man who said to you, "Take it up and walk"?' Now the man who had been healed did not know who it was, for Jesus had disappeared in the crowd that was there

(John 5: 2–13)

Burra sets his painting inside the pool at Bethesda where the five porticos can be made out. A massive Roman bath-like structure covers the pool. Jesus in a brown robe addresses the infirm man, who lies, in a blue robe, in the extreme bottom right corner. There is no sign of the angel, or the disturbed waters, but the pool is crowded with ill and infirm people and their helpers. Burra links illness with evil, peopling the pool with ghoulish and fearful faces (particularly the man held on his back with his face upside down, looking out of the picture at the front left and the two monkey-like figures at the extreme right).

Burra painted a series of large watercolours of biblical scenes in the early 1950s, of which The pool of Bethesda is one. In his book on Burra (Edward Burra. Complete Catalogue, Phaidon Press Ltd, London 1985) Andrew Causey comments that these paintings were 'isolated in their emotional intensity from what either preceded or followed them'. Causey continues that 'Burra wanted above all to express passion. Even when, as in The pool of Bethesda, the role of Jesus is a healing one, he has the intense, possessed features of a shaman.' (Shaman: a priest who attempts to exorcise evil spirits.)

When it was exhibited at the Lefevre Gallery in 1963, from which it was bought for the Methodist Collection, Terence Mullaly, writing in the Daily Telegraph described the painting as 'a remarkable technical tour de force and a picture of alarming emotional impact ... Yet this picture is more than a display of virtuosity. The strange setting, the use of colour, and the many tortured figures contribute to an impression which places the most pessimistic and horrific of interpretations upon the story of the pool of Bethesda.'

Indeed it is difficult to reconcile the imagery with the basically positive, healing, story of the miracle at Bethesda recorded in the Bible. Burra's interpretation is very different in response and feeling from Murillo's calmer, more traditional approach, now in the National Gallery in London.

© *RW*

Mark Cazalet

Born: London 1964

Studied: Chelsea School of Art 1982–3; Falmouth School of Art 1983–6; Ecole des Beaux Arts, Paris (French Government Scholar) 1986–7; M S University, Baroda, India (Commonwealth Scholarship) 1988–90

Selected commissions: Stations of the Cross, The Church of the Good Shepherd, Brighton 1992; Millennium window, Worcester Cathedral 1999.

Selected collections: Museum of London; Guildhall Art Gallery, London

**5 Nathaniel
(asleep under the fig tree)**
Oil on paper, 1993, 18 cm by 18 cm.

When Jesus saw Nathaniel coming towards him, he said of him, 'Here is truly an Israelite in whom there is no

5

deceit!' Nathaniel asked him, 'Where did you come to know me?' Jesus answered, 'I saw you under the fig tree before Philip called you'. Nathaniel replied, 'Rabbi, you are the Son of God! You are the King of Israel!' Jesus answered 'Do you believe because I told you that I saw you under the fig tree? You will see greater things than these.' And he said to him, 'Very truly, I tell you, you will see heaven opened, and the angels of God ascending and descending upon the Son of Man.'

(John 1: 47–51)

Cazalet portrays Nathaniel lying down on the ground under the fig tree, prior to his calling by Philip. He is shaded by the foliage and lies apparently naked. The ground is sketched in beneath him, with the dappled shadow of the fig tree. The tree is not botanically accurate but fits the

artist's purpose in portraying the fig tree as an image of fruitfulness and consistency.

The artist has tried not only to capture the nub of the story, particularly Nathaniel's bizarre response to Jesus' comment, but also to suggest that there was something unusual about the narrative. Cazalet suggests that Nathaniel knew that Jesus had seen him in his entirety, 'through all the trappings, nothing was hidden, all was exposed and acknowledged'. In the simplicity of the composition (a figure, a few marks to indicate the ground and a few more to indicate the tree), Cazalet has captured the simplicity of the story, the 'metaphysical moment when every part of Nathaniel was "seen" by Christ'.

The story of Jesus' encounter with Nathaniel is an unusual subject for

6

a painting. The artist knows of no other versions and there are no well-known paintings of the subject by the Old Masters. Cazalet was simply intrigued by the story. The modelling of the figure, which is coloured an unrealistic deep reddy-brown, is very sculptural and three-dimensional, drawing on the impact of 'primitive' or 'tribal' art (African, Pacific Island, American and Inuit, etc) on twentieth-century art. Early Epstein, Gill, Moore, Barbara Hepworth and Eric Dobson sculptures are particularly relevant in this respect.

6 Fool of God (Christ in the Garden)
Oil on paper, 1993, 18 cm by 18 cm.

And he came out, and went, as was his custom, to the Mount of Olives; and his disciples followed him. And when he reached the place, he said to them, 'Pray that you may not come into the time of trial.' Then he withdrew from them about a stone's throw, knelt down, and prayed, 'Father, if you are willing, remove this cup from me; yet not my will, but yours be done.' Then an angel from heaven appeared to him and gave him strength. In his anguish he prayed more earnestly, and his sweat became like great drops of blood falling down on the ground.

(Luke 22: 39–44)

Cazalet portrays Jesus at prayer, leaning against a rock in the spare landscape. He does not clutter the picture or heighten the tension within it by including the angel or the other disciples or by seeking to convey the agony of Jesus physically in any way. The title of the painting refers to the idea of 'Holy Fools', familiar to us particularly from Russian literature and history as those who 'set God's will above worldly wisdom, even to the point of martyrdom'.

The figure of Jesus is portrayed with a single serpentine brush stroke which captures the bend in his back over the convenient rock and the reddy-brown colour contrasts in tone and hue with the greens and olives of the landscape with its tree, scrub, rocks and path. The artist contrasts the figure of Jesus with that of Isaac, bound by his father before being sacrificed, held against his will but later released; Jesus is here held of his own free will by his mission on earth, although he is technically free to run away. Cazalet has sought to capture the 'moment of (Christ's) most profound incarnation, fully in dread at the fate he knew would come as a man, yet faithful and obedient in his divine fulfilment of the sacrifice'.

These two biblical paintings (and others in the series) were painted between December 1993 and January 1994 as a result of Cazalet's daily meditations. After reading and re-reading the Bible he decided that he did not want merely to illustrate the stories but to get to the kernel of each, to convey what God was trying to reveal through the character's situation, the universal truths behind the familiar drama. This purpose was helped by the use of hand-made paper with a cockled surface, which the artist enjoyed using immensely.

7

topic, two ways of approaching it, two sides of it or two appearances in different contexts.

© *RW*

Eularia Clarke

Born: London 1914
Died: Southampton 1970

Studied: Ruskin School, Oxford

Selected commissions: The Last Supper, Catholic Chaplaincy, Southampton University 1962

7 The five thousand
Oil, 1962, 65 cm by 62 cm.

Now when Jesus heard this, he withdrew from there in a boat to a deserted place by himself. But when the crowds heard it, they followed him on foot from the towns. When he went ashore, he saw a great crowd; and he had compassion for them and cured their sick. When it was evening, the disciples came to him and said, 'This is a deserted place, and the hour is now late; send the crowds away so that they may go into the villages and buy food for themselves.' Jesus said to them, 'They need not go away; you give them something to eat.' They replied, 'We have nothing here but five loaves and two fish.' And he said, 'Bring them here to me.' Then he ordered the crowds to sit down on the grass. Taking the five loaves and the two fish, he looked up to heaven, and blessed

His decision to work on a small scale heightens the impact of each painting and, with the paper, results in a rich precious feel for the works, so meeting his objective of a highly condensed, powerful summary of each subject.

Cazalet's work is figurative but not naturalistic. There is always something behind the surface appearance. 'Any story with metaphor or allegory will interest me – an equivalent or parallel reading.' He is variously trying to capture the essence of a paradox, an epiphany or a moment of revelation and as such is offering his testimony, his insight into the subject at the time he produced the work. This is true not only of his religious work but also of his secular subjects which are often paired to give two views of the same and broke the loaves, and gave them to the disciples, and the disciples gave them to the crowds. And all ate and were filled; and they took up what was left over of the broken pieces, twelve baskets full. And those who ate were about five thousand men, besides women and children.

(Matthew 14:39-44)

Eularia Clarke sets the feeding of the five thousand in modern dress and follows Matthew's account in which women and children are present. The multitude has sat down in the grass, as Jesus requested, and is eating, not the fish and bread referred to in the Bible but, as in so much of Clarke's work, a twentieth Century equivalent, fish and chips. The scene is more reminiscent of a church picnic than the biblical miracle. Tea is brewing in the lower right corner, bicycles and footballs are discarded, children and babies are remarkably well behaved, some people doze, others pay attention to the priest – or Jesus (whose head and shoulders are uncomfortably cut off by the edge of the painting).

8 Storm over the lake
Oil, 1963, 62 cm by 62 cm.

One day he got into a boat with his disciples, and he said to them, 'Let us go across to the other side of the lake.' So they put out, and while they were sailing he fell asleep. A gale swept down on the lake, and the boat was filling with water, and they were in danger. They went to him and woke him up, shouting, 'Master, we are perishing!' And he woke up and rebuked the wind and the raging waves; they ceased, and there was a calm. He said to them, 'Where is your faith?' They were amazed, and said to one another, 'Who then is this, that he commands even the wind and water and they obey him?'

(Luke 8: 22–25)

Jesus is shown leaning forward, calming the storm. The boat is in extreme danger of being swamped, with several people already swept overboard and near to death. The crew have had the presence of mind to reef the sail when the storm arose. The blue, black and white pillow (looking more like a travelling rug) on which, according to Mark, Jesus was sleeping, is portrayed in the stern of the vessel.

Eularia Clarke came from a long

8

line of artists (Gainsborough's sister was an ancestor) and parsons. 'I knew no religion except polite formalities', she wrote in 1968. 'Yet I was obsessed by it, and trailed around after "High" services, wondering what it was all about ...' She drew and painted from childhood, as did all her family, and decided she wanted to be a religious painter when she was very young after visiting Saint Mark's in Venice while on holiday. She studied theology at Oxford and studied painting in her spare time at the Ruskin School, a training in the basics that she later felt had been immensely valuable, and which she enjoyed and felt was more relevant than her theology course.

She spent the next twenty-five years or so bringing up a family and teaching art in schools. In 1959 she was received into the Catholic Church and the following year went on a pilgrimage to Lourdes. Feeling progressively more dissatisfied with her experiences there, she raised the subject in confession and received some reassurance that God would give something of his grace to her. As she left the church she saw the pilgrims coming up to the church as if they had been painted by Stanley Spencer. From that moment on she produced a stream of religious paintings, although she only valued a few from each year's production (four in 1960, one in 1961, five in 1962, three in 1963 but increasing to

twelve in 1967 and thirteen in 1968). Like Stanley Spencer (and influenced by him, for his work gave her the idea of 'bashing through those palm-tree settings and flowing robes which make the gospel incidents seem so local in both time and space') she set her paintings in the twentieth century

among ordinary people pursuing their lives. As a result, her work was often mistaken for that of Spencer, which she felt was an honour and advantage when ordinary people (rather than the cognoscenti) were looking at it.

Her life, once her children had

9

grown up and she had separated from her husband, became rather eccentric. She drove around the country in a mini-van, living in it as if in a caravan, and finding inspiration for her work in the most unlikely places. The idea for The five thousand, for example, came from people eating fish and chips on Canvey Island – she started thinking about the subject as she ate her own fish and chips. At first she felt unable to paint the figure of Jesus, 'I am too frightened to paint Christ except as a baby, or facing away…' She says with regard to The five thousand, 'I daren't paint Christ, I put in a pulpit, the priest is reading the notices before the sermon.'

Of the following year (1963), she writes, 'Near the end of a very rough school term, the schoolboys seemed to be drowning me like stormy waves. I come home too tired to do anything except paint the experience out in this painting of the storm on the lake. It is a relief to be able to put Christ in. I keep praying, "This is meant to be your Son, don't let him look like just any ordinary human." I wouldn't be dragged all that way to Mass by a man who just lived and taught a long time ago.'

Eularia Clarke did not usually sell her paintings. In letters in 1965 she said 'now people keep trying to buy the Gospel paintings to have in their homes – often quite agnostic people who just like them as paintings. I have worried and prayed a lot about this, and finally decided to keep them as a collection for lending … It's awfully awkward about private buyers – I had a hunch that I'd better resist them, right at the start, and only sell to exhibitions and public institutions, the remainder forming a nucleus of a collection … It's interesting that several private offers had been resisted for both the paintings you chose!' Storm over the lake was on loan to a Catholic priest who 'does his meditation from it and uses it for sermons' and initially she did not have the heart to ask for it back.

© *RW*

Roy de Maistre

Born: Bowral, New South Wales, Australia 1894 **Died:** 1968

Studied: Royal Art Society of New South Wales 1913–16; Sydney Art School, Australia 1916

Selected commissions: Crucifixion 1945 and Stations of the Cross 1953 at Westminster Cathedral (RC), London; Resurrection, Chaplaincy Centre, Oxford 1950; paintings, Immaculate Heart of Mary (RC), Hayes, London 1961; Paintings at St Aidan's Church (RC), East Acton, London 1964; Iona Cathedral (RC)

Selected collections: Tate Gallery, London

9 Noli me tangere (Touch me not)
Oil, 1952–8, 95 cm by 67 cm.

But Mary stood weeping outside the tomb. As she wept she bent over to look in the tomb; and there she saw two angels in white, sitting where the body of Jesus had been lying, one at the head and the other at the feet. They said to her, 'Woman why are you weeping?' She said to them, 'They have taken my Lord, and I do not know where they have laid him.' When she said this she turned around and saw Jesus standing there, but she did not know that it was Jesus. Jesus said to her, 'Woman, why are you weeping? For whom are you looking?' Supposing him to be a gardener, she said to him, 'Sir, if you have carried him away, tell me where you have laid him, and I will take him away.' Jesus said to her, 'Mary!' She turned and said to him in Hebrew 'Rabboni!' (which means Teacher). Jesus said to her, 'Do not hold on to me for I have not yet ascended to the father. But go to my brothers and say to them, "I am ascending to my Father and your father, to my God and your God." Mary Magdalene went and announced to the disciples, 'I have seen the Lord'; and she told them he had said these things to her.

(John 20: 11, 14–18)

The figure of Jesus, facing us, towers over the kneeling Mary Magdalene, who has her back towards us. It is still early in the morning and the sky is red with sunrise. The warm red-brown colour of both the landscape and Mary contrasts with the cool blues, white and greys of Jesus and the rocky garden. The mouth of the tomb, in a reddish stone or brick, is visible on the left, with marks that can be read as 'LO'.

In addition to this painting, there are two or three other versions of 'Noli me tangere', the largest and earliest dating from 1950–1, painted for the Arts Council's Festival of Britain exhibition '60 Painters for 51', with the others (as well as the Methodist work) being much smaller.

10 The supper at Emmaus
Oil, 1958, 60 cm by 50 cm.

10

Now on that same day two of them were going to a village called Emmaus about seven miles from Jerusalem … While they were talking and discussing, Jesus himself came near and went with them, but their eyes were kept from recognising him… Then one of them, whose name was Cleopas, answered him, 'Are you the only stranger in Jerusalem who does not know the things that have taken place there in these days.' He asked them, 'What things?' They replied, 'The things about Jesus of Nazareth, who was a prophet mighty in deed and word before God and all the people …'

Then he said to them, 'Oh how stupid you are, and how slow of heart to believe all that the prophets have declared! Was it not necessary that the Messiah should suffer these things and then enter into his glory?' Then, beginning with Moses and all the prophets, he interpreted to them the things about himself in all the scriptures. As they came near the village to which they were going, he walked on ahead as if he were going on. But they urged him strongly, saying, 'Stay with us, because it is almost evening and the day is now nearly over.' So he went in to stay with them. When he was at the table with them he took the bread, blessed and broke it, and gave it to them. Then their eyes were opened, and they recognised him; and he vanished from their sight. They said to each other, 'Were not our hearts burning within us while he was talking to us on the road, while he was opening the scriptures to us?'

(Luke 24: 13, 15-16, 18-19, 25-32)

De Maistre shows Jesus, in a white gown, positioned centrally at the table with one of his disciples on the left and the other sitting at the side of the table. Jesus is breaking the bread and has an apple (or some other green fruit) in front of him. More fruit (including a pear and black grapes) lie on a plate or bowl on the table. The disciples are portrayed just as recognition dawns on them that their companion is Jesus. The wounds, the nail hole in Jesus' left hand and the wound of the spear in his side are clearly visible and confirm their realization.

In 1958 de Maistre was one of several artists approached by St Edmund Hall in Oxford to paint a 'Supper at Emmaus' for the college chapel. Ceri Richards was eventually selected. The Methodist Collection includes a study of this painting, dating from 1958 (see entry number 26). Perhaps this version of the Supper at Emmaus (which has certain similarities to the Richards and provides an interesting comparison) is related to the commission for they were both painted in 1958.

It is possible, however, that they are unconnected because de Maistre, a practising Roman Catholic, was a prolific painter of religious subjects, producing multiple versions of the Crucifixion and several sets of Stations of the Cross. In an interview in The Times in 1959, De Maistre commented that 'religion is not merely a subject for a painting but a perpetual reality which has preoccupied me ever since I remember and is inseparable for me from every other thought'.

Little known during his life (the catalogue for his 1960 retrospective drew attention to his unfamiliarity among the general public and the scant attention he received from the art world as well), de Maistre is perhaps largely forgotten today. Yet he is an important figure in the twentieth-century art history of his native Australia, and also in Britain (he lived in England from 1938 until his death in 1968). Initially as interested in music as art (he studied both), some of his early work was concerned with the relationship between music and art and he developed an interest in colour which has been compared to a musical approach and which continued to inform his work throughout his life.

He developed a very personal style, combining elements from cubism and traditional realism and can be regarded as one of the century's major religious artists, successfully tackling the difficult task of painting religious works which are contemporary in idiom but which can stand alongside the masterpieces of the past that so colour and influence our expectations.

© *RW*

Michael Edmonds

Born: Dorset 1926

Studied: Cardiff School of Art 1944–7 (part-time); Royal West of England Academy School of Architecture, Bristol 1947–53

Selected commissions:
mural, Llandough Hospital Pneumoconiosis Unit near Cardiff 1958; fonts for Wesley's Chapel and Methodist Missionary Society Chapel, London 1963 (carved from steps on which Nathaniel Gilbert stood to denounce slavery in Antigua); panel and contemplative cross/mandala for International House, Penarth (now in Trinity Methodist Church, Penarth) 1965; external mural, Methodist Church, Stockport early 1970s

11 The cross over the city
Polyester, brass and mosaic, relief panel, 1962, 150 cm by 90 cm. Signed and dated bottom right.

The only work in the Collection concerned with the Church's mission, rather than with the biblical story of Jesus' life and the festivals of the Church, The cross over the city superimposes an upright cross, with a strong black horizontal, upon an array of 130 rectangular red blocks. The upright of the cross is made from a combination of a thin black strip at the top, narrow white border strips at the bottom with two rows of white and coloured mosaic squares. From a distance it looks like an aerial photograph of traffic on a major road crossing a road or railway cutting, both passing through a rigidly uniform estate of urban housing blocks (equally at home in America, Russia or a municipal housing estate in western Europe). The reflective gold, black, red, green, yellow and blue mosaic tesserae together with some areas of 'gold-dust' speckled on a dark surface at the top, give a precious feeling of sparkling richness to the relief.

Although he was keen from the first to be an artist, circumstances led Michael Edmonds to qualify as an architect and to work in private practice for some twenty years before joining the Greater London Council in 1973, retiring in 1980 to devote himself full-time to painting (largely in watercolours). In the 1960s and early 1970s he produced a number of constructions and sculptures using mixed media including glass fibre and cast aluminium.

Michael Edmonds has commented that he has never seen religion and science as opposed (any more than he has felt figuration and abstraction to be opposites – indeed he has used both in his work). He is a 'convinced Christian but not exclusive' and much indebted to Eastern quietude.

© *RW*

11

12

24

Elisabeth Frink

Born: Thurlow, Suffolk 1930
Died: 1993

Studied: Guildford School of Art 1947–9; Chelsea School of Art, London 1949–52

Selected commissions: Blind beggar and dog, Bethnal Green, London 1957; eagle lectern, Coventry Cathedral 1962; J F Kennedy Eagle Memorial, Dallas 1964; altar cross, Liverpool Cathedral 1966

Selected collections: Tate Gallery, London; British Museum, London; Scottish National Gallery of Modern Art, Edinburgh; Fitzwilliam Museum, Cambridge; Birmingham City Museums and Art Gallery

12 Pieta
Drawing, December 1956, 85 cm by 68 cm. Signed and dated bottom right.

After these things, Joseph of Arimathea, who was a disciple of Jesus, though a secret one because of his fear of the Jews, asked Pilate to let him take away the body of Jesus. Pilate gave him permission; so he came and removed his body. Nicodemus, who had at first come to Jesus by night, also came, bringing a mixture of myrrh and aloes, weighing about a hundred pounds. They took the body of Jesus, and wrapped it with the spices in linen cloths, according to the burial custom of the Jews. Now there was a garden in the place where he was crucified, and in the garden there was a new tomb in which no one had ever been laid. And so, because it was the Jewish day of Preparation, and the tomb nearby, they laid Jesus there.

(John 19: 38–42)

The Pieta (Lamentation), normally portrayed as the sorrowing Virgin alone (or with other mourners) with the body of her dead son, is a subject for devotional meditation rather than a strict portrayal of the biblical narrative. In these terms, Elisabeth Frink's drawing is of the Deposition rather than a Pieta. The dead Jesus is shown, still crowned with thorns, after Joseph of Arimathaea has taken his body down from the Cross (often portrayed as 'The Descent from the Cross') but before wrapping him in the linen cloth and placing him in the sepulchre or tomb. Jesus is shown as if propped up against a rock, with his right arm extended upwards as it would be if Joseph were placing him gently in a sitting position on the ground.

Alternatively, perhaps, this drawing is a study for a pieta, which would have included the figure of the Virgin Mary as well. In later pietas, Jesus is usually shown lying on the ground with head raised, or the Virgin Mary is shown removing the crown of thorns from the dead Jesus' head. If the Methodist Pieta was a study, it was for a work which was not produced or an idea which was not developed.

Elisabeth Frink commented 'I think I did a lot of drawings that were all entitled "Pieta" which, to me, has nothing to do with whether the Virgin Mary was represented or not. Why should she always be in a Pieta? These are details of the Christ from a "Pieta" – he is obviously dead and in a recumbent position. I would not call it a "Deposition" because he is not being lifted down by anybody.'

Although best known as a sculptor, Frink's graphic work is considerable, encompassing watercolours, drawings, lithographs and book illustrations, and including both independent works and studies for sculptures. With regard to the latter she commented that 'my illustrations have nothing to do with sculpture, neither activity helps the other, because the illustrations are subjective and my sculptures are not.' The drawings have much in common with the sculptures in the sense that they have the same power and strength. 'I am incapable of making little drawings. I always draw big ... I attack the paper with large sweeping forms ...' It is certainly true that both the Methodist Pieta and a similar work dating from two years later (currently in the collection of the Marquess of Aberdeen and Temair) have great strength and power, for the figures are massive and overflow from the sheet of paper.

It is interesting to note that, writing in 1963, Elisabeth Frink said that it was one of her favourite drawings from the 1950s.

© *RW*

Eric Gill

Born: Brighton 1882
Died: Harefield, London 1940

Studied: Chichester Technical and Art School 1897

Selected commissions: Stations of the Cross, Westminster Cathedral, London 1913; Leeds University War Memorial 1922–3; London Underground Railway (London Transport), Broadway, London 1928–9; BBC, Broadcasting House, London 1929–31; St Peter Apostle, Gorleston, Norfolk 1939

Selected collections: Tate Gallery, London; Scottish National Gallery of Modern Art, Edinburgh; Ashmolean Museum, Oxford; Birmingham City Museum and Art Gallery; Ditchling Museum, Sussex; Hove Museum and Art Gallery; Leeds University Collection; Manchester City Art Gallery

13 Annunciation
Watercolour on paper, c. 1912, 9 cm by 12 cm.

In the sixth month the angel Gabriel was sent by God to a town in Galilee,

13

called Nazareth, to a virgin engaged to a man whose name was Joseph, of the house of David. The virgin's name was Mary. And he came to her, and said, 'Greetings, favoured one! The Lord is with you.'

(Luke 1: 26–28)

Gill sets the Annunciation indoors, in Mary's bedroom. The Angel Gabriel, in a multicoloured robe (red, yellow and blue) rather than the usual white, stands unshod in front of Mary who kneels before him. She is wearing a black jacket and hood, a blue blouse and a red skirt with blue-soled slippers and black socks. Gabriel holds a lily with another in a vase behind Mary. (The lily signifies that the Annunciation took place in the Spring and symbolizes Mary's purity.)

The yellow/orange-and-white chequer pattern on the floor is repeated in the blue-and-white chequer pattern of the bed-covering and the panes of glass in the window, which opens on to a rich, deep blue sky. Unusually in paintings of the Annunciation, the Holy Spirit is not included (it usually appears as a dove or ray of light).

At first sight it appears odd that the text of Gabriel's message 'Ave Maria' ('Hail Mary') and Mary's reply 'Fiat mihi' ('Let it be unto to me') appears back to front. Mary's reply to the angel is indeed sometimes written upside down so that it can be read by God in Heaven, but it is unusual to find the text written backwards. It transpires that the Annunciation was produced for projection through a mirrorscope.

In 1912 (and in following years, but not earlier as far as is known) Eric Gill presented a Christmas 'slide' show in the living room of his home, Hopkins Crank, at Ditchling in Sussex, using a mirrorscope. This was a variation on the magic lantern – a sort of early overhead projector which had twin mirrors illuminated by acetylene burners and which projected opaque images rather than requiring transparent ones. It could project black and white photographs, pictures cut from publications and original drawings which were reversed in projection, so that any text would come out the right way round. (This information comes from a letter to the author from Peter Cribb, son of Joseph Cribb, who was Eric Gill's first assistant appointed in 1906 as a fifteen-year-old. Joseph Cribb operated and serviced the mirrorscope, which continued in use in the Cribb family after the Gills had left Ditchling for Wales in 1924.) The exhibition of Gill's work held at the Alpine Club Gallery in London in 1916 or 1918 included six 'designs for lantern slides'.

The son of a Protestant clergyman, Gill became a Roman Catholic in 1913 and in due course became perhaps not so much 'a Catholic artist' as 'the Catholic artist', a label, as Fiona MacCarthy says in her biography, (Eric Gill, Faber and Faber, London 1989) that 'both belittled his achievement and in a sense reduced his possibilities'. Throughout his life Gill pursued a very personal approach to religion, one difficult to reconcile with the attitudes and teachings of the organized Church, particularly the Catholic Church. Yet perhaps more than any other twentieth-century British artist, one feels that his religious beliefs informed his whole life and work.

Gill's achievements are substantial in the three media he pursued – lettering and inscription, sculpture, and drawing and graphic work. In each of these he maintained a simplicity of line and form that, as in this Annunciation, was inspired by late medieval and early renaissance art (see John Physick, Catalogue of the Engraved Work of Eric Gill, London 1963 and Evan R Gill, The Inscriptional Work of Eric Gill, London 1964).

© *RW*

Susie Hamilton

Born: 1950, London.

Studied: St Martin's School of Art 1969-72; London University 1978-87 (BA and PhD in English Literature); Byam Shaw School of Art 1989-92.

Selected collections: Murderme, UK; Deutsche Bank, London; Bernard Jacobson, London; The Groucho Club, London; The Economist, London; St. Giles Church, Cripplegate, London.

14 Ecce Homo
Acrylic, 1999, 15 cm by 21 cm. Signed on the reverse

Then Pilate took Jesus and had him flogged. And the soldiers wove a crown of thorns and put it on his head, and they dressed him in a purple robe. They kept coming up to him, saying, 'Hail, King of the Jews!' and striking him on the face. Pilate went out again and said to them, 'Look, I am bringing him out to you to let you know that I find no case against him.' So Jesus came out, wearing the crown of thorns and the purple robe. Pilate said to them, 'Here is the man!' When the chief priests and the police saw him, they shouted, 'Crucify him! Crucify him!' Pilate said to them, 'Take him yourselves and crucify him; I find no case against him.'

(John 19: 1 -7)

'Ecce Homo' is Latin for 'Here is the man' (or 'Behold the man' as it appears in some versions of the Bible). It has been an important subject in Christian art from the 9th century onwards, and in the last two centuries has been extended beyond the representation of Jesus to the portrayal of suffering and the degradation of humans through violence and war.

This is a study for a number of much larger works on the same theme. A lone figure stands with arms outstretched and the torso forms a vertical axis in the centre

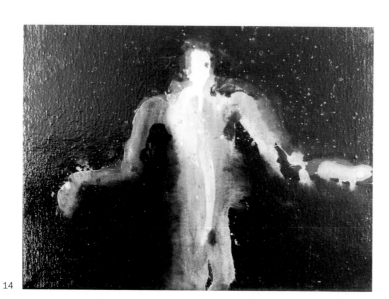

14

15

of the canvas. The openness of the posture demonstrates vulnerability and acceptance. Richard Dyer observes, while "the condition conveyed by the posture of the body … is one of helplessness, the image also contains the possibility of transcendence." (From 'All that is solid melts into Light' by Richard Dyer in 'Susie Hamilton: New Work' by Paul Stolper, 2000).

Susie Hamilton has described the creative process: "In 1999 I took part in Paul Stolper's Cab Gallery project for which I made books of drawings from the back of a moving taxi. The speed of drawing led to attenuations and distortions of the figure creating a sense of its fragility or brokenness. It was this quality that I decided to emphasise in the series of paintings that followed and which were called Mutilates–a name

I invented to suggest both mutilation and mutation. The paintings are of white figures on black grounds, composed of many thin layers of watery acrylic. Paint is poured, floated, blown with a hairdryer in order to create a see-through effect of cells, veins and tissues. The semi-transparent, 'photographic negative' effect indicates conflicting or complementary ideas about humanity. On the one hand there exists the decaying, dissolving body and on the other, the idea of spirit or soul. The paintings set up a tension between the material (of paint or bodies) and the idea of the immaterial. In the Ecce Homo series, streaming veils of paint can express bursts of exuberance or traumatic disintegration. The figure can be seen ambivalently as rising or plummeting, suggesting the

possibility of Resurrection as against the certainty of death."

Hamilton has commented further: "In a way these Mutilates are atypical of my work because they are black and white. Generally my painting is to do with bursts of light and bright, sharp colour. I suppose this use of light and colour expresses a view of life which could be called religious in the sense that I attempt to represent the creatures in my work as part of a dangerous but gorgeous world of energy which is also glittering with the possibility of being "charged with the grandeur of God" (Gerard Manley Hopkins). I like to start in nature but heighten and intensify and make things other, strange, supernatural or surreal. In the end I suppose that I incline towards the religious (in people, literature, thought) because it doesn't shut down or limit consciousness but, to quote Hopkins on the music of Purcell, it 'fans fresh our wits with wonder'."

Dennis Hawkins

Born: Epsom 1925
Died: Derbyshire 2001

Studied: Ruskin School 1947–9, Slade School of Art 1949–52

Selected commissions: cross, St Wystan's Church (crypt), Repton; crucifixion, Repton School 1979–80

Selected collections: Victoria and Albert Museum, London; Birmingham City Museum and Art Gallery; Fitzwilliam Museum, Cambridge

15 Pentecost I

Oil on wood (old school desk), 1962, 107 cm by 80 cm.

When the day of Pentecost had come, they [the apostles] were all together in one place. And suddenly from heaven there came a sound like the rush of a violent wind, and it filled the entire house where they were sitting. Divided tongues, as of fire, appeared among them, and a tongue rested on each of them. All of them were all filled with the Holy Spirit and began to speak in other languages, as the Spirit gave them ability.

(Acts of the Apostles 2: 1–4)

Pentecost I is one of three related versions of the subject produced in the early 1960s. This, the first, is by far the most effective. The descent of the Holy Spirit, which took place ten days after the Ascension on the Jewish feast of Pentecost, and which marked the birth of the Church, is represented by an intense circle of white light, painted on the top of an old school desk. In this way he represents the success of the Church penetrating unlikely nooks and crannies and dark corners throughout the world and illuminating them with the light of the Holy Ghost.

Hawkins' painting is, however, much more complex than this description suggests. The circle of light shares the old desk lid with a black vertical (offset from the centre) and two white verticals (one at each edge), and the right-hand third or so of the desk is lightly painted white, as is a series of indentations along the bottom edge, under the circle. The desk lid itself is placed off-centre on a light brown (fawn) board with a thick band of black paint extending just above the desk almost the whole way across the board, with just a small gap on the extreme left. The black band is painted a short distance down from the top of the brown board and the intervening area is painted white for a little over half its width (stopping – or starting – roughly level with the centre of the circle of light). Finally the brown board itself is mounted on an unpainted white base-board.

Dennis Hawkins spent his whole working life as Director of Art at Repton School in Derbyshire. In addition to his school work he occupied an important place in British printmaking in the second half of the twentieth century, being a founder member of the Printmakers Council, and its Chairman in 1971–2.

The Pentecost series brings together a number of his principal concerns: reinterpreting 'stories' from the past, a great emphasis on colour, the use of familiar objects, and repetition of subject matter. In the 1960s he produced dozens of Pentecosts. The traditional iconography of Pentecost was tongues of fire, but instead of these Hawkins chose to use the circle or sphere as his symbol. He had used the form often before, after seeing the famous pictures of Earth from space. He saw the disk as a numinous object, mysterious without beginning or end and all-embracing, an ideal symbol for the coming of the Holy Ghost.

© RW

Albert Herbert

Born: London 1925
Died: 2009

Studied: St Martin's School of Art, London 1942; Wimbledon School of Art 1947–49; RCA, London 1949–53

16

16 Epiphany
Oil, 1962, 77 cm by 65 cm.

In the time of King Herod, after Jesus was born in Bethlehem of Judea, wise men from the East came to Jerusalem, asking 'Where is the child who has been born King of the Jews? For we observed his star at its rising and have come to pay him homage.'

(Matthew 2: 1–2, 11)

A very dark, rich painting of blues, reds and browns. The three Magi, not richly apparelled as kings, but perhaps rather wise, old men, at the extreme left of the painting, make their way along the track leading to the stable where the baby Jesus in his manger is shown with Mary in a well-lit glowing interior. The simple, four-square gabled stable building stands at the edge of the track.

Epiphany, January 6th, is one of the six festivals that structure the Church year (the others being Christmas, Good Friday, Easter, Ascension and Pentecost). In the Eastern Church it celebrates the baptism of Jesus while in the Western Church it is concerned with the manifestation of Jesus to the Gentiles through the Magi's worship of the baby Jesus. Among Germanic peoples in the first millennium, Epiphany was celebrated as the Feast of the Three Holy Kings.

Albert Herbert had no interest in religion or religious subjects until he was in his thirtieth year. Initially he exhibited with the 'Kitchen Sink' school and met the Italian New Realists. He has said since that he 'was never really quite happy with depicting the appearances of things' and his pictures became 'increasingly introspective, more about states of mind than the external world'.

In 1959 he was received into the Catholic Church. At that time he produced many religious paintings. Simple paintings of mothers and children developed into 'Mother and Child' paintings, in due course placed, as in the Methodist painting, in a 'Holy House'. Some of these were shown with an upper room in which it could be deduced the Eucharist was being celebrated (so called Eucharistic Houses). The Methodist painting falls into this category but does not have the Upper Room, the Magi taking its place as a secondary focus of attention.

When he moved to London in 1964 Herbert found the ethos at St Martin's School of Art, with its emphasis on avant-garde modernism, antagonistic to his religious painting.

As a result he began to doubt both his religious beliefs and his paintings of religious subjects. In 1982 he decided (though he comments 'I don't know why') to return to overtly biblical subjects (initially as etchings, later as paintings) and returned to the Church as a practising Catholic. A few students took note of his resulting work but it was generally ignored until late 1986 when he started getting offers of exhibitions and started selling again, sales which have continued to the present.

© *RW*

Patrick Heron

Born: Leeds 1920
Died: Zennor, Cornwall 1999

Studied: Slade School of Fine Art, London 1937–9.

Selected commissions: stained glass window, Tate Gallery, St Ives 1992

Selected collections: Tate Gallery, London; Victoria and Albert Museum, London; Scottish National Gallery of Modern Art, Edinburgh; National Museum of Wales, Cardiff; Leeds University Collection; Manchester City Art Gallery

17 Crucifix and Candles: Night 1950
Oil, 1950, 51 cm by 41 cm. Signed and dated top left corner.

17

The painting, set at night, shows a crucifix between a pair of burning candles, standing on a table or altar in front of a leaded window. The painting has 'a pronounced linear charcoal drawing on white primed canvas which the flat washes of oil colour edged up to without hiding. They were all fixed with charcoal fixative, which acted almost like re-touching varnish on the areas of oil colour.'

Heron has said that when he painted Crucifix and Candles he was fascinated by Titian's The

18

Ghislaine Howard

Born: Eccles, near Manchester, 1953

Studied: Department of Fine Art, Univ. of Newcastle upon Tyne 1972-1976

Selected commissions: The Stations of the Cross / The Captive Figure; The Visitation Altarpiece, Liverpool Hope University College; The Saint Anthony Cycle, private collection, North Yorks

Selected collections: Manchester City Art Gallery; Whitworth Art Gallery; Graves Art Gallery, Sheffield; Salford City Art Gallery; Saint Mary's Maternity Unit, Manchester; the Manchester Metropolitan University; Her Majesty's Prison Service; British Medical Association; The Royal Collection.

18 The Washing of the Feet
Acrylic on canvas, 2004.
102cm x 127 cm.

And during supper Jesus knowing that the Father had given all things into his hands, and that he had come from God and was going to God, got up from the table, took off his outer robe, and tied a towel around himself. Then he poured water into a basin and began to wash the disciples'

Vendramin Family in the National Gallery in London. Titian's painting of the brothers Gabriel and Andrea Vendramin and Andrea's seven sons, includes a crucifix and a pair of candles on an altar. The crucifix is a reliquary for a fragment of the True Cross which had been rescued by a member of the family when in danger of falling into a canal. The Heron crucifix bears a schematic, linear figure of Jesus but the cross is substantial enough also to be a reliquary.

Heron was an exceptional figure in twentieth-century British art, well known as both a painter and a critic. In the mid-1960s he moved from a predominantly figurative approach to abstraction, and he remains best known today for his abstract explorations of colour and form. Crucifix and Candles: Night 1950 dates from shortly before his first abstract experiments in 1953.

Whether painting figurative or abstract works Heron has always been concerned with 'pictorial experience' rather than 'illustration' or seeking a realistic portrayal of any subject. As he has said, 'I am not a member of any church. The painting was made as a result of a purely pictorial experience only.' In that sense this is not an overtly religious painting.

© *RW*

feet and to wipe them with the towel that was tied around him. He came to Simon Peter, who said to him, 'Lord, are you going to wash my feet?' Jesus answered, 'You do not know now what I am doing, but later you will understand'. Peter said to him, 'You will never wash my feet.' Jesus answered, 'Unless I wash you, you have no share with me.' Simon Peter said to him, 'Lord, not my feet only but also my hands and my head!' After he had washed their feet, had put on his robe, and had returned to the table, he said to them, 'Do you know what I have done to you? You call me Teacher and Lord - and you are right, for that is what I am. So if I, your Lord and Teacher, have washed your feet, you also ought to wash one another's feet.

(John 13: 2b – 9, 12- 14)

The figures are set against a rich green/blue background and completely dominate the composition. Their gestures and the rhythms of their bodies focus attention on the most crucial moment of the narrative. Howard has mixed sand with the paint to create a sculptural surface texture which serves at once to unify and heighten the intensity and intimacy of the scene. Here are two real figures each in their different ways reacting to one of the most poignant and moving episodes in the Gospels.

The Methodist Collection has many works on the Passion Narrative but has not previously included an interpretation of Jesus washing the disciples' feet. In 2004, the Trustees of the Collection approached Ghislaine Howard, an artist well known for her strong, physical portrayals of the human figure and for her ability to express the Christian faith in an imaginative and arresting way. Having given her complete artistic freedom, the Trustees were delighted that the picture suggests the Middle Eastern origins of the Christian faith as reflected in the shape of the bowl and the warmth of the skin tones. The importance of the event is conveyed by the classical and monumental style which echoes earlier interpretations of the theme. The dress is simple and workman-like; these two figure figures could be from any age and any country. The simple, everyday act of washing a guest's feet before offering hospitality becomes through the words and actions of Jesus a moment pregnant with significance.

Ghislaine Howard is best known for her ground-breaking work on pregnancy and birth. A painter of powerful and expressive means, she has shown her large cycle of paintings, 'The Stations of the Cross/ the Captive Figure', to great acclaim at the two Liverpool Cathedrals, Canterbury Cathedral and Gloucester Cathedral.

© *T*

Francis Hoyland

Born: Birmingham 1930

Studied: Camberwell School of Art, London 1947–1950; Slade School of Art, London 1950–1

19 Nativity polyptych
Oil, 1961, 90 cm by 120 cm.

And she gave birth to her firstborn son, and wrapped him in bands of cloth, and laid him in a manger; because there was no place for them in the inn. In that region there were shepherds living in the field, keeping watch over their flock by night. Then an angel of the Lord stood before them, and the glory of the Lord shone around them: and they were terrified. But the angel said to them, 'Do not be afraid: for, see, I am bringing you good news of great joy, for all the people.'
(Luke 2: 7–10)

The Massacre of the Innocents: When Herod saw that he had been tricked by the wise men, he was infuriated and he sent and killed all the children in and around Bethlehem who were two years old or under …
(Matthew 2: 16)

See also entry numbers 16 and 28 for Biblical texts.

Strictly speaking a polyptych is a painting with four or more folding leaves. By its nature it therefore has four (or, taking into account the fact

19

that two leaves have two sides each,
six) surfaces to paint and allows
the artist to present a number of,
usually related, subjects. Hoyland has
retained the name and the multiplicity
of subjects but has used only a
single panel, creating an effect more
like a narrative icon that has a large
central image of a saint, surrounded
by a series of smaller scenes from
his or her life.

In his Nativity polyptych, Hoyland
has flanked the central image of the
nativity with four small images and
one large predella-like image across
the whole width of the panel. The
central scene shows the baby Jesus
in the manger, with a lantern above,
and Mary (in a blue gown) propped
up against the manger under a brown
cloak and Joseph (in a reddish-
brown gown) asleep under a brown
cloak on the floor. The stable looks
very much like a contemporary farm
building. On the top left there is the
announcement to the shepherds; top
right shows the journey of the Magi
(three very unregal figures, back-
packing, through a dangerous-looking
Lickey Woods in Birmingham, towards
their guiding star). Bottom right is the
Flight into Egypt (to escape Herod's
murderous paranoia) with Mary in
her blue gown carrying the child

and Joseph pushing a pram through Richmond Park.

The Massacre of the Innocents that they are fleeing is portrayed in the other two panels. The bottom left panel represents the Massacre by a nuclear attack, with buildings in flames and a dead baby in the road, while the wider 'predella' panel shows the Massacre in terms of the contemporary warfare raging in the Congo at the time Hoyland painted the polyptych.

20 Holy communion predella
Oil, 1961, 32 cm by 195 cm.

For I received from the Lord what I also handed on to you, that the Lord Jesus on the night that he was betrayed took a loaf of bread, and when he had given thanks, he broke it and said, 'This is my body that is for you. Do this in remembrance of me.' In the same way he took the cup also after supper, saying, 'This cup is the new covenant in my blood. Do this, as often as you drink it, in remembrance of me. For as often as you eat this bread and drink the cup, you proclaim the Lord's death until he comes.'

(The First Letter of Paul to the Corinthians 11: 23–26)

Francis Hoyland has chosen in this painting to set the whole subject in the twentieth century amid episodes from his familiar, everyday life. In an altarpiece, the predella is the painted panel placed underneath the main picture – often with a series of subsidiary scenes as here. Hoyland's central scene shows a priest celebrating Communion in a Gloucester church, offering the bread and wine to the communicants. The scene on the far left portrays the birth of Hoyland's youngest son in a bedroom at his home, with the midwife and the father standing in front of a cot; the second scene from the left shows the baptism of his eldest son taking place in the Gloucester church also seen in the central panel; the second scene from the right shows the Hoyland family eating an al fresco tea (with milk bottle and bread on the table); while the right-hand scene takes the personal odyssey from birth to death with the artist's father, John Hoyland, a well-known Quaker leader and writer, on his death bed at home. His son and other members of the family and a nurse are in attendance.

21 Crucifixion polyptych
Oil, 1962, 120 cm by 90 cm.

And when they had crucified him, they divided his clothes among themselves by casting lots; then they sat down there and kept watch over him. Then two bandits were crucified with him, one on his right and one on his left. Those who passed by derided him, shaking their heads.

(Matthew 27: 35–36, 38–39)

Meanwhile, standing near the cross of Jesus were his mother and his mother's sister, Mary the wife of Cleopas, and Mary Magdalene. When Jesus saw his mother and the disciple whom he loved standing beside her, he said to his mother. 'Woman, here is your son.' Then he said to the disciple, 'Here is your mother.' And from that hour the disciple took her into his own home.

(John 19: 25–27)

20

21

The Crucifixion polyptych follows a similar pattern to the Nativity polyptych, with the central scene of the crucifixion surrounded by eighteen small panels. Of these, four are larger and represent other episodes in the crucifixion story, the others (seven on each side) represent the stories of the Good Samaritan (right) and the Prodigal Son (left).

In the Crucifixion, St John stands to the left of Jesus and Mary to the right as Jesus addresses John. The detail captured in the crucifixion is accurate, with the weight of the body stretching Jesus' arms down, rather than with both arms held horizontally (as in gymnastics on the rings). The setting is clearly an English landscape rather than Golgotha.

Below, in descending order, are represented the Last Supper, with Jesus giving his disciples bread and wine; Jesus in prayer on the Mount of Olives with the two sleeping disciples in the background; the Betrayal in the Garden of Gethsemane, with Judas in the act of kissing Jesus; and the entombment, with Joseph of Arimathaea and Nicodemus carrying the body of Jesus to the sepulchre.

The portrayal of the Good Samaritan (Luke 10: 30–35) is set in Richmond Park and shows the stages of the story in episodes from top to bottom with the traveller being mugged and left for dead. A priest and another passer-by (the Levite) avoid him but the Good Samaritan helps him and calls an ambulance which takes him to hospital.

The story of the Prodigal Son (Luke 15: 11–32) is also told in a series of episodes from top to bottom. At the top, the son leaves home; sexual gratification is followed by a scene of penitence in the countryside; then return by bicycle to his father's home; a scene of reconciliation and welcome; the meal with the fatted calf (although the meal appears rather more meagre); and finally a further reconciliation or perhaps the father talking with the other son.

For Francis Hoyland painting and religion are intimately intertwined:, 'I continue to paint as an act of worship and faith …'

Jacques Iselin

Born: France 1933
Died: 2003

Studied: Ecole Nationale Supérieure des Beaux-Arts, Paris

22 The Elements of the Holy Communion
Oil, 1963, 180 cm by 105 cm. Signed bottom right.

See entry number 20 for Biblical Text.

22

Iselin's painting was commissioned especially for the Collection. It is a development of ideas which the artist had started exploring in three small gouache studies. The 'elements' of the Holy Communion are the bread and wine used in the ceremony. The painting explores the elements and their origins. The studies gave prominence to the chalice (used for the wine) and the bread (in the form of a long loaf). In the painting Iselin has added to these elements the ears of wheat from which the bread is made, a number of mysterious and half-hidden objects and a fish, perhaps as a symbol (drawing on the natural world) of Christ who is present in the Communion.

The fish has an added relevance as a Christian symbol. The Greek word for fish, IXO-YΣ, is made up from the initial letters of the Greek words Jesus, Christ, of God, the Son, Saviour. In this way it combines the literary aspect of the liturgy with the mysterious presence of Christ in the ceremony of Holy Communion. The 'elements' are portrayed and explored in this painting against a rich bright background of yellow, orange and red, very much akin to the rich textiles often used as an altar frontal or priest's vestments at a Holy Communion service.

While not a traditional representational painting this is not an abstract work, but a symbolic, figurative exploration of the central

mysteries of the Church and Christianity. The elements (in both senses) are clearly visible for all to see.

Although born in France, Iselin lived in England from 1956 and taught art at the Lycée Français in London for many years.

© RW

David Jones

Born: Brockley, Kent 1895
Died: Harrow 1974

Studied: Camberwell Art School from 1909 to 1914; Westminster School of Art in 1919

Selected collections: Tate Gallery, London; Imperial War Museum, London; National Museum and Gallery of Wales, Cardiff; National Galleries of Scotland; Birmingham Museum and Art Gallery; Brecknock Museum and Art Gallery; Ditchling Museum; Leeds University Collection

23 Three Kings
Engraved woodblock, 1925,
10cm by 8cm

See entry number 16 for Biblical text

The woodblock was made for a Christmas card while David Jones was living at the Capel-y-ffin community created by Eric Gill in the Black Mountains of Wales. The local

hills feature prominently and below them lies Bethlehem illuminated by the rays of the star. The three kings are on foot with their heads slightly bowed, while near them is a mutilated tree. David Alston has suggested that this tree both foreshadows the Crucifixion and reflects Jones' experience in the battlefields of the First World War. The words, inscribed in reverse, 'Omnes de Saba Venient' are known from early Epiphany carols and come from the prophecy of Isaiah (Chapter 60 v6): 'All shall come from Sheba bringing gold and frankincense, and showing forth praise to the Lord'.

David Jones' father, James, was from North Wales but moved to London to work as a printer. There he met and married Alice, a Londoner born and bred. From an early age David wanted to be an artist and at fourteen he persuaded his parents to let him attend art school. On the outbreak of the First World War, he enlisted with the Royal Welch Fusiliers and served on the Western Front right through until 1918. 1921 was for him a crucial year: not only was he was received into the Roman Catholic Church but he met Eric Gill, joining his community first at Ditchling, Sussex, and then at Capel-y-ffin. Arrival in the Black Mountains stimulated his latent interest in Welsh culture and landscape, the latter being captured in many evocative watercolours. At the same time, he had the stimulus of working in a community dedicated to an integration of religion and art; the sacred and the ordinary. As he himself put it 'you can never tell when the Holy Ghost is going to turn something inside out'.

His wood engravings were highly regarded but later in life he seems to have lost interest in the medium. He developed a unique mixture of pencil and watercolour resulting in dense works full of symbolism. He also devised what he termed "painted inscriptions" and these are much admired by enthusiasts for calligraphy

In addition David Jones is well known for his writing, particularly his 1937 prose poem 'In Parenthesis' that draws on his First World War experiences. He wrote a number of essays. One, "Art and Sacrament", included in Epoch and Artist (Faber, 1959), explores the meaning of signs and symbols in everyday life and relates them to Roman Catholic teachings. He argues that the unique ability of human beings to make works of art is a God-like quality.

© **T**

Philip le Bas

Born: St Quentin de Baron, near Bordeaux, France 1925

Studied: Regent Street Polytechnic, London; Brighton College of Art

Selected commissions: Stations of the Cross, Our Lady of the Visitation, Greenford, Middlesex (RC) 1961; mural of St Dominic Savio, St Dominic Savio, Hawley, Farnborough, Hampshire (RC) 1962

24

24 The stripping of our Lord
Oil, 1962, 58 cm by 50 cm.

Then the soldiers of the governor took Jesus into the governor's headquarters, and they gathered the whole cohort of soldiers around him. They stripped him, and put a scarlet robe on him.

(Matthew 27: 27–28)

Jesus stands upright, naked to the waist with a white cloth from the waist down. A soldier in armour stands behind him on his left, with his head and helmet bent forward as he strips him, whilst Jesus looks towards a distant horizon.

This painting is related to a series of painted Stations of the Cross commissioned from Le Bas for the Church of Our Lady of the Visitation at Greenford in west London (see also entry number 30). The Stations (illustrated in the book by David Konstant, The Way of the Cross, Catholic Trust Society, London 1984) were for a new church, built in 1961, and were commissioned by the architect, David Stokes.

Writing shortly after completing the painting, Le Bas said, 'I have tried to show, without sentiment, the sufferings of a man, as I feel in this way the average person will come closer to realizing what agony and loneliness Christ must have endured.'

By the mid-1960s Le Bas was getting no further religious commissions and his religious paintings were not selling. Influenced by the success and abstract style of his friend from college days, Patrick Reyntiens, the stained glass-maker and designer, Le Bas turned to abstraction himself and produced a series of abstract works, all of them religious and drawing on the

25

saleable than his figurative religious works. He therefore returned to realist painting, in time hyper-realist, concentrating on the everyday world and producing series of paintings of hotels, stations, theatres, Hollywood stars and food. These have all sold extremely well.

© *RW*

Theyre Lee-Elliott

Born: Lewes, Sussex 1903
Died: London 1988

Studied: Central School of Art and Design, London 1925–7

Selected collections: Victoria and Albert Museum, London

25 Crucified tree form – the agony
Tempera and gouache, 1959, 85 cm by 65 cm. Signed and dated bottom left.

See entry number 21 for Biblical text.

Theyre Lee-Elliott's Crucified tree form draws on a tradition dating from the thirteenth century in which the cross on which Jesus is crucified is a living tree. In this painting Lee-Elliott has developed the 'living tree' one stage further and created a crucifixion which conveys 'the agony' with the head and shoulders falling forward and the arms stretched up backwards, in a V (as in Francis Hoyland's Crucifixion polyptych). The cross, tree and body are fused

symbolism of the 'host' (the bread consecrated in the Eucharist), tabernacle or ciborium (a canopied shrine in which the Eucharist is kept). The paintings, which combined the

host with the head of a figure or a church, were described by Le Bas as 'large ... swashbuckling ... large areas'. However, he found that these abstract paintings were no more into a single suffering whole. A modern touch is added with the strands of barbed wire. In fact there is something of the First World War battlefield about the painting; the dead trees, now a familiar icon of the twentieth century, add an additional resonance to the work.

Although the son of an Anglican clergyman, Theyre Lee-Elliott was an agnostic, if not an atheist, throughout his life. This painting is part of a lengthy series of 'quasi-religious' paintings Lee-Elliott produced shortly after he had been gravely ill in hospital in Leyden, Holland in 1959. An article in a west London newspaper in 1962, 'Chelsea Artists' by MH, comments of that illness: 'he fell extremely ill with food poisoning and although he did not know this until afterward, was for a short time close to death. When he eventually recovered he had an insatiable desire to paint a picture in which the wood of the cross met the same point as the crucified body itself ... This he has done and achieved some success.'

His sister, Monica Sacret, commented in 1992 : 'Theyre was definitely not a practising Christian, and I am pretty sure he was not a believer, though undoubtedly he did have deep feelings of some kind in the 1960s when he did these pictures. I remember him telling me it was just something he felt he had to get out of him.'

Lee-Elliott said in a letter in 1962, 'since a child I have been excited by

26

the potential human shape within trunks and branches. [The] painting comes closest, perhaps, to the contortion of agony which, in my search to find the point at which the wood of the cross and the agony of Christ met, was my objective.' In the 1962 'Chelsea Artists' article Lee-Elliott is recorded as saying 'When I was a child I had a strange feeling about trees ... I felt that they had more life than inanimate objects ... I used to believe that the trunk of the tree was like the body and the branches were arms and that a tree grew like a human being grows.'

© *RW*

John Muafangejo

Born: Lo Mghadi, Southern Angola 1943 **Died:** Namibia 1987

Studied: Rorke's Drift Art School, Natal, RSA 1964

Selected collections: British Museum, London

26 Judas Iscariot betrayed our Lord Jesus for R.3.00
Linocut 1972 34cm by 45cm. Signed. Print no 37 of 100

While he was still speaking, Judas, one of the twelve, arrived; with him was a large crowd with swords and clubs,

27

27 Israel, Jews, Christians, Heathen, Our God for all People
Linocut 1981 35cmx 33cm. Signed Print no 23 of 150

As many of you as were baptized into Christ have clothed yourselves with Christ. There is no longer Jew or Greek, there is no longer slave or free, there is no longer male and female; for all of you are one in Christ Jesus. And if you belong to Christ, then you are Abraham's offspring, heirs according to the promise.

Galatians 3.27-29

In this work there are two images of Christ, both of them half black and half white. In the upper one he stretches out his robed arms, while in the lower one, the same arms are naked on the cross. The diversity of the faces in between shows that all are received without distinction. The universality of God's love was a theme to which the artist kept returning.

Muafangejo's homeland of Ovamboland stretches across what he described in one of his pictures as an 'artificial boundary' between Angola and Namibia. After the death of his father in 1956, he trekked across the border to Odibo in Namibia where he received a formal education at St. Mary's Anglican Mission. It was there that his outstanding artistic talent was recognised, and it was from there

from the chief priests and the elders of the people. Now the betrayer had given them a sign, saying, 'The one I will kiss is the man; arrest him.' At once he came up to Jesus and said, 'Greetings, Rabbi!' and kissed him. Jesus said to him, 'Friend, do what you are here to do.' Then they came and laid hands on Jesus and arrested him

Matthew 26.47-50

When Judas, his betrayer, saw that Jesus was condemned, he repented and brought back the thirty pieces of silver to the chief priests and the elders. He said, 'I have sinned by betraying innocent blood.' But they

said, 'What is that to us? See to it yourself.' Throwing down the pieces of silver in the temple, he departed; and he went and hanged himself.

Matthew 27.3-5

This work is divided into two parts. On the right a clean-shaven Judas is shown embracing Jesus while two bearded figures, with weapons in their hands and sheathed swords, look on. They must be part of the high priest's entourage. On the left Judas is shown hanging from a tree: three rand notes, the price of betrayal, can be seen below the foliage.

that he was sent by Bishop Mallory to study at the art school at Rorke's Drift in Natal. While Muafangejo was still a student, the art critic Edward Lucie Smith encouraged and helped him to organise his first exhibition in Durban. Throughout his career, he worked almost exclusively in lino cut, producing powerful images filled with events: autobiographical, social, political and Biblical. In general, earlier works are more detailed in their structure than later ones, the latter often being simpler and more dramatic in their appeal.

Muafangejo wanted his works to 'teach.....to pass on a message'. Not only do his lino-cuts illustrate the beauties of the flora and fauna of Southern Africa and the activities of local people, but also, most tellingly, they chronicle events such as the destruction of church property and the deportation of church leaders under the harsh apartheid regime of his time. They also show vividly his deep Biblical knowledge and Christian commitment. This is clearly demonstrated in the two works in the Collection, which span much of Muafangejo's short working life (1968 - 1987).

During his last few years, John Muafangejo exhibited in major one-man exhibitions all over the world. On the occasion of an exhibition at London's Commonwealth Institute in 1983, his work prompted comparison with David Hockney and with the German expressionist masters of woodcut: Ernst Ludwig Heckel, Erich Kirchner and Karl Schmidt-Rottluff. He died suddenly and tragically on November 27th 1987 shortly after returning to Namibia from a triumphant one-man exhibition at London's Royal Festival Hall. Soon after his death, his work was seen by hundreds of millions of viewers world-wide when his images were used as a backdrop at the Wembley Concerts celebrating the 70th birthday of Nelson Mandela (1988), and a free South Africa (1990). These same images on their vast canvases were used a few years later during the Namibian Independence celebrations.

Much of the above comes from a commentary written by the Rev John Wheeler on an exhibition of prints 'African Harmony' that was shown from 29 June - 14 July 2000 at the Africa Centre, London. It was from John Wheeler that the prints in The Methodist Collection were acquired.

© *T*

28

Nicholas Mynheer

Born: Oxford 1958

Studied: Hornsey College of Art, London 1977-81

Selected commissions:
sculpture, Birmingham Cathedral; sculpture, Newcastle Cathedral; windows, Methodist Church House, London; window, St. Martin's Church, Tuddenham, Suffolk; paintings, St. Matthew's Church, Perry Beeches, Birmingham; painting, St. John's College Chapel, Oxford; sculpture, Sir Harold Hillier Arboretum, Hampshire

28 Rest on the Flight to Egypt
Oil on canvas, 2003. 20 x 50 cm.

Now after they (the wise men) had left, am angel of the Lord appeared to Joseph in a dream and said, 'Get up, take the child and his mother, and flee to Egypt, and remain there until I tell you; for Herod is about to search for the child, to destroy him.' Then Joseph got up, took the child and his mother by night, and went to Egypt, and remained there until the death of Herod. This was to fulfil what had been spoken by the Lord through the prophet, 'out of Egypt I have called my son.'

(Matthew 22: 13-15)

Mynheer portrays the Holy Family taking a moments rest in the shade of a tree. With the threat of Herod receding, Mary and Joseph are able to play with the baby Jesus.

The artist writes 'I remember being told that the Judean Desert blooms with wild flowers for about two weeks every spring. I had the idea that as the Holy Family travelled across the desert it flowered in response to the presence of The Lord. Even the tree under which they are seen resting has come into fruit; for Nature itself responds to God, praising in its own way. This picture encapsulates my own faith for it seems to me that man is not separate from Nature and the world but rather part of it. God is to be found in everything around; in the clouds, the mountains, the trees and animals, even the stones and dust. All these things glorify God in their own way. In the words of The Benedicite: 'O All ye Works of the Lord, bless ye the Lord: praise him, and magnify him forever '. When I paint, sculpt stone or work with glass I stylise and simplify. Anything that I feel is not essential to the design is omitted and anything deemed important is emphasised. If I use a background in a painting it is never just a backdrop; the very landscape is involved in the event portrayed; trees might act as pointers, clouds move in response or buildings enfold or lean away.'

© *T*

John Reilly

Born: 1928 **Died:** Isle of Wight, 2010

Studied: Kingston on Thames Art College 1949–52

Selected collections:
Leicestershire County Council Education Department; Findhorn Foundation; Gaunts House, Wimborne, Dorset (long-term loan)

29 Cain and Abel
Oil, 1958, 92 cm by 124 cm. Signed and dated bottom right.

Now the man knew his wife Eve; and she conceived and bore Cain, saying, 'I have produced a man with the help of the Lord.' Next she bore his brother Abel. Now Abel was a keeper of sheep, but Cain was a tiller of the ground.

In the course of time Cain brought to the Lord an offering of the fruit of the ground, and Abel for his part brought of the firstlings of his flock, their fat portions. And the Lord had regard for Abel and his offering, but for Cain and his offering he had no regard. So Cain was very angry, and his countenance fell. The Lord said to Cain, 'Why are you angry, and why has your countenance fallen? If you do well, will you not be accepted? And if you do not do well, sin is lurking at the door; its desire is for you, but you must master it.'

So Cain said to his brother Abel, 'Let us go out to the field.' And when they were in the field, Cain rose up against his brother Abel, and killed him. Then the Lord said to Cain, 'Where is your brother Abel?' He said, 'I do not know; am I my brother's keeper?' And the Lord said, 'What have you done? Listen; your brother's blood is crying out to me from the ground! And now you are cursed from the ground, which has opened its mouth to receive your brother's blood from your hand. When you till the ground, it will no longer yield to you its strength; you will be a fugitive and a wanderer on the earth.'

(Genesis 4: 1–12)

Cain's fenced farmland, under intensive cultivation, and Abel's extensive sheep runs are clearly delineated in the rolling landscape. The acceptance of Abel's gift of a sacrificial lamb is represented by a bright and open area in which he and his herds are placed, with a vortex of light representing God's acceptance of his gift, which descends from heaven and bathes him in its glow. Cain, in contrast, is in a closely defined, darker area, with his rejected sheaf of corn. He directs a murderous look at Abel while digging his land. Reilly has placed his portrayal of Cain and Abel at the point between the gifts to God and the murder. Cain's anger and hate are visibly conveyed by his demeanour, look and stocky stature (in stark contrast to Abel's tall, willowy grace).

30 The feeding of the five thousand (Miracle of loaves and fishes)
Oil, 1958, 81 cm by 122 cm. Signed and dated bottom right.

See entry number 7 for Biblical text.

30

Reilly divides the miracle into three, sequentially from right to left. On the right we see a group of four people with the seven loaves and four fish which was all that was available to feed the multitude of four or five thousand men, women and children. In the centre the figure of Jesus, in shirt and trousers, is illuminated from above and the light is deflected from and through him to the same group of four, on the left, where, after the miracle has occurred, there are enough fish and loaves to feed everybody.

Reilly has taken the accounts in the Gospels of St Matthew (15: 32–38) and St Mark (8: 1–9) which both record that there were 'seven' loaves, rather than the 'five' included in the other two accounts. The lack of faith in Jesus' ability to feed the multitude is conveyed in the right-hand group by placing them in a dark umbra, and

they are shown disturbed and worried that there is not enough to eat. An unusual, decorative sun (in addition to the source of the light descending on Jesus) shines on the miracle, from the top left corner, in a deep blue sky. All the figures are dressed in casual clothes of indeterminate period (although some are transparent) and the overall impression to a late twentieth-century viewer might be that they are South American, Indian or Middle Eastern peasants or workers.

31 The healing of the lunatic boy
Oil, 1958, 67 cm by 106 cm. Signed and dated bottom right.

When they came to the crowd, a man came to him, knelt before him, and said, 'Lord, have mercy on my son: for he is an epileptic and he suffers terribly; he often falls into the fire and

often into the water. And I brought him to your disciples, but they could not cure him.' Jesus answered, 'You faithless and perverse generation, how much longer must I be with you? How much longer must I put up with you? Bring him here to me.' And Jesus rebuked the demon, and it came out of him: and the boy was cured instantly.
Matthew 17:14 –18

As in his miracle of the loaves and fishes (see previous entry), Reilly places Jesus and his works, in this case the healed boy, in a golden yellow light. By contrast, those in the everyday, 'fallen' state of humankind (the boy, in one of his lunatic fits, between the two disciples who tried and failed to heal him) are cocooned in a dark and dismal world.

32 The raising of Lazarus
Ripolin enamel, 1962, 81 cm by 102 cm. Signed bottom right.

So they took away the stone. And Jesus looked upwards and said, 'Father, I thank you for having heard me. I knew that you always hear me, but I have said this for the sake of the crowd standing here, so that they may believe that you sent me'. When he had said this, he cried with a loud voice, 'Lazarus, come out.' The dead man came out, his hands and feet bound with strips of cloth, and his face was wrapped in a cloth. Jesus said to them, 'Unbind him, and let him go.'
(John 11: 41–44)

Set in a typical English churchyard (the church with its tower on the left, a backdrop of trees and an array of gravestones), the raising of Lazarus is conveyed with a centrifugal vortex as Lazarus (on the left) is resurrected by Jesus (on the right). Martha and Thomas are both shown twice at the head of the grave, and the blood-red setting sun provides a powerful focus around which the scene revolves. The imagery draws on photographs taken with fish-eye wide-angle lenses and high speed photography which differentiates a series of positions of a single subject.

When the Methodist Collection was formed, John Reilly wrote in a letter, 'All the ideas for my paintings over the last ten years have come from the Bible – I have painted the same subject many many times and will no doubt go on doing so until I get what I want.'

A practising Christian (he has said that Christianity is 'the leading interest in my life – it is my life'), John Reilly is not a member of any organized church ('My church is all about me all the time'), although he is a student of the works of Mary Baker Eddy,

32

the founder of the Christian Science movement, and of her teachings based squarely on the Bible.

© *RW*

Ceri Richards

Born: Dunvant, Swansea, Wales 1903 **Died:** London 1971

Studied: Swansea College of Art 1921–4; Royal College of Art, London 1924–7

Selected commissions: Supper at Emmaus, St Edmund Hall, Oxford 1958; Deposition, St Mary's Church, Swansea 1960; stained glass windows, Derby Cathedral 1964–5; tabernacle, reredos and windows for the Chapel of the Blessed Sacrament, Liverpool RC Cathedral 1968

Selected collections: Tate Gallery, London; Victoria and Albert Museum, London; National Museum of Wales, Cardiff; Whitworth Art Gallery, Manchester; Glynn Vivian Art Gallery, Swansea, Wales; Leeds University Collection; Walker Art Gallery, Liverpool; Manchester City Art Gallery; Pallant House, Chichester

33 The supper at Emmaus

Gouache, 1958, 40 cm by 40 cm. Signed and dated bottom right and inscribed along the bottom edge:

'drawing of altar piece – The Supper at Emmaus, Chapel of St Edmund Hall, Oxford University.'

See entry number 10 for Biblical text.

The altar piece at St Edmund Hall was a commission, the result of

invitations to five artists (including two others represented in the Methodist Collection, Lee-Elliott and de Maistre) to submit proposals for a painting of this subject.

Jesus sits facing the viewer, looking out of the picture, with one disciple sitting opposite him (with his back to

33

the viewer) and one on the right. The table is represented schematically in contrast to the chair directly in front of us, which is a modern-looking, sturdy piece of furniture with four bars across the back. A jug, a goblet and two plates (one with three bread rolls on it) can be seen on the table. The whole scene is portrayed in blues, yellows and greens.

The drawing is largely an accurate version of the altar piece. The most noticeable differences are in the colour of the clothing of the disciple on the right (a bright ultramarine in the altar piece compared with a dirty bluish-green in the drawing); in the altar piece, the disciple with his

34

back to us has tilted his chair in his reaction to the sudden recognition of Jesus and the background has some areas of changed colour. The other important variation is that the body of Jesus is sketched (in black outline) and is more noticeable in the drawing than in the altar piece where his yellow robe merges into the yellow background (which forms part of a yellow cross that is central to both paintings).

Both works date from 1958 and there are two studies (one an initial 'design idea' and the other a 'colour sketch') at St Edmund Hall. The design idea is very similar to the final work compared with the Methodist drawing, while the colour sketch differs significantly in the choice of colours from the other drawings and the painting.

In creating the collection Douglas Wollen had been moved by Richard's two religious works, The Deposition in Swansea and the Supper at Emmaus at St Edmund Hall. He contacted Richards about the possibility of a further commission for the Methodist Collection. At the time Richards was just about to exhibit at the 1962 Venice Biennale and was committed to his first Marlborough show (June 1963). He commented that he was 'profoundly interested in the religious subject … I approach these subjects with great care and circumspection for I cannot decide casually to just "do" a religious subject.' In another letter he mentioned that he had

'a small gouache study of the St Edmund Hall Supper at Emmaus painting and a very unfinished second version of a Deposition.' The Emmaus study was chosen and added to the Methodist Collection.

© *RW*

William Roberts

Born: Hackney, London 1895
Died: London 1980

Studied: St Martin's School of Art, London 1909; Slade School of Art, London 1910–13

Selected collections: Tate Gallery, London; Imperial War Museum, London; Leeds University Collection; Manchester City Art Gallery

34 The crucifixion
Oil, early 1920s, 75 cm by 90 cm. Signed bottom left.

See entry number 21 for Biblical text.

The scene is set on a hill top (with a wall running behind the place of execution), with the roofs and domes of Jerusalem in the background. The composition of the painting is unusual in the way Roberts has placed the three crucified figures. It is usual to show them in a line, with Jesus in the centre (as the Gospels record), but Roberts has grouped them on the right of the painting (as we look at it) in a tight triangle. Jesus appears as the left-hand figure, although he remains central if you look at them from either left or right of the painting.

At the foot of his cross the soldiers are casting lots for his garments; on the left, four Roman soldiers are holding back the crowd (one man has climbed on his companion's shoulders to get a better look); there is, in the group on the right, a man dressed in brown/black who may be taken to be a representative of the Jewish authorities. Around the foot of the cross there are three figures – one in yellow, one bearded in brown and one in grey. A fourth figure, in blue and brown, with his back to the viewer, is in an ambiguous position. He is wearing boots similar to those worn by the Roman soldiers, and is kneeling towards the soldiers casting lots, but with his body twisted towards the cross and his arms raised towards Jesus. Perhaps he is the Centurion (already being affected by the presence and bearing of Jesus) or perhaps he is just one of the soldiers casting lots (although his shirt is blue rather than red like the other soldiers) and is merely gesturing at Jesus. The figure near the cross in grey looks like a woman (blonde hair and red lips) and is probably Mary, the mother of Jesus. However, the way in which the grey robe has fallen forward suggests that it might be a man rather than a woman.

The painting captures a moment shortly after the crucifixions had begun. The two thieves are in pain (there is no apparent distinction between the penitent and the impenitent thief) but Jesus is tight-lipped with the growing agony; there is no wound in his side, so the lance has not yet injured him and his cross carries no inscription (perhaps it has yet to be put up).

Roberts is one of the leading early twentieth-century British artists, a member of the Vorticist movement with Wyndham Lewis, Edward Wadsworth and Henri Guadier-Brzeska.

In the catalogue for the Roberts' retrospective show at the Tate Gallery in 1965, Ronald Alley records that Roberts recalled painting the Methodist Crucifixion 'shortly after the end of his service as a war artist, at a time when he had some idea of entering for the Prix de Rome ... A little later Rudolph Stalik, proprietor of the nearby Restaurant de la Tour Eiffel, came to his studio and told him that he thought he had found a buyer for it. Roberts did not discover until afterwards that this was Augustus John.' The painting remained in the collection of the painter Augustus John from around 1923 until 1963 when it was sold by his estate, after his death, and acquired for the Methodist Collection.

© **RW**

35

Peter Rogers

Born: London 1933

Studied: St Martin's School of Art, London 1954–6

35 The mocking of Christ
Oil, 1961, 112 cm by 187 cm. Signed bottom left, dated bottom right.

Then the soldiers of the governor took Jesus into the governor's headquarters, and they gathered the whole cohort around him. They stripped him and put a scarlet robe on him, and after twisting some thorns into a crown, they put it upon his head. They put a reed in his right hand and knelt before him, and mocked him, saying 'Hail King of the Jews!' They spat on him, and took the reed, and struck him on the head.

(Matthew 27: 27–30)

Jesus is seated to the left, crowned with thorns and holding the reed, and wearing a purple robe (Mark and John describe the robe as purple, Matthew as scarlet). Eight Roman soldiers are grouped around him in various mocking acts – the leftmost raises his right arm to strike Jesus, one stands in front of him with arms outstretched, two on the right 'bow the knee', and one lies on the floor, as if exhausted by the mockery.

Strictly speaking Rogers has portrayed not the 'Mocking of Christ' but the 'Crowning with Thorns'. The

36

and only practical way of erasing evil and suffering from the face of the earth. They do not merely depict historical events, but represent the state to which all men today should surely aspire if the world is to avoid what, for the first time in history, may quite literally be hell-fire ... I still believe that "Thy kingdom" can and will "come on earth as it is in heaven", that heaven ought to be experienced here as well as hereafter, but that heaven is a state of consciousness and that, once that state has been found within, it will inevitably manifest itself without.' These are views that Rogers still holds today and they reveal clearly that his 'quest' has been of a piece from the early 1960s right through to today.

36 The ascension
Oil, 1963, 125 cm by 100 cm. Signed and dated bottom right.

So when they had come together, they asked him, 'Lord, is this the time when you will restore the kingdom to Israel?' He replied, 'It is not for you to know the times or periods that the Father has set by his own authority. But you will receive power when the Holy Spirit has come upon you; and you will be my witnesses in Jerusalem, in all Judea and Samaria, and to the ends of the earth.'

When he had said this, as they were watching, he was lifted up, and a cloud took him out of their sight. While he was going and they were gazing up

two incidents are separate. The mocking takes place after Jesus' appearance before Caiaphas and is by Jews rather than Roman soldiers. Jesus is usually blindfolded and has his hands tied. There is no crown of thorns or purple (or scarlet) robe and no reed, all of which are present in the 'Crowning' which takes place with Roman soldiers after the appearance before Pilate. It is not unusual for the two incidents to be combined in a single painting.

The mocking of Christ stands somewhat apart from the majority of Rogers' other paintings of the early 1960s, perhaps forming part of the first cycle of the Life of Jesus. The background is minimal and the majority of the figures are Roman soldiers (with similarities to the Roman soldier in the 1960 Crucifixion Triptych) and the portrayal of the scene is more straightforwardly realistic than most of the other paintings.

Rogers said of the Life of Jesus cycle, 'these pictures depict the one *towards heaven, suddenly two men in white robes stood by them. They said 'Men of Galilee, why do you stand looking up into heaven? This Jesus, who has been taken up from you into heaven, will come in the same way as you saw him go into heaven.'*

(Acts 1: 6–11)

In the centre of the picture Jesus ascends in a whitish-gold cloud, his body already off the ground, arms raised upwards and his head thrust back, almost horizontally, in profile, in a style reminiscent of William Blake. On the left, the two men clad in white are standing in the embrace of a deep-red flame that descends from the heavens and curves beneath them, while on the right a group of disciples, undifferentiated except perhaps for Mary in a brown robe, gaze upwards as Jesus is lost to view within the cloud and ascends to heaven. This all takes place against a black and inky background with a faint glow on the horizon.

Rogers' whole life has been concerned with spiritual and religious painting. His first religious work was a Crucifixion (1957) painted shortly after leaving Art School. It was three or four years later that he produced his next overtly religious paintings. In 1960 he had a religious experience or vision at a concert in the Royal Albert Hall in London. He saw a woman walking towards him, a group of tightly knit people gazing up and between them a kneeling woman, also looking up. A great glowing ball of light rolled into his field of vision and hovered above the central kneeling figure. There was also the sound of waves breaking on a seashore. Rogers interpreted his vision as the Ascension.

Rogers' painting draws on Christian (he remains a Christian, but not a church member, believing that joining encourages separation rather than oneness), Buddhist and Classical ideas, and on recent scientific thinking. In a letter in 1992 Rogers says of his Ascension paintings that they embody his 'conception of Christ as what I call "the channel of awareness." This concept is based on such remarks by Jesus as "I of my self can do nothing, the Father within he does the works." In other words, the Christ is the channel for, rather than the initiator of, "the works". For it is my belief that Jesus acted out the life of Christ as it pertains to individual you and me. So when he said "No man comes to the Father except by me", far from bolstering any sense of exclusivity all he was saying was that no one can find God other than through their own channel of awareness.' He comments that the Methodist Ascension is 'the most graphic depiction – perhaps the most graphic I've ever painted – of my conception of Christ as "the channel of awareness".' (See also Peter Roger, A Painter's Quest', Bear & Co, Santa Fe, USA, 1987.)

© **RW**

Frank Roper

Born: Haworth, Yorkshire 1914
Died: Penarth 2000

Studied: Keighley School of Art; RCA, London 1936–9

Selected commissions: St Martin and the Beggar, Stations and other work for St Martin's Church, Roath, Cardiff from 1957; Stations of the Cross for St Saviour's Church, Splott, Cardiff 1963; Hanging Crucifix, Peterborough Cathedral 1973–4; Lady Chapel Reredos and other work, Llandaff Cathedral; Alington Memorial, Durham Cathedral 1979; Reredos, Grimsby Parish Church; Stations of the Cross, St Leonard's Church, Doncaster; Crucifixion, St German's Church, Cardiff

Four reliefs from a set of Stations of the Cross
Aluminium (lost wax casting), 1963. Unsigned. Nos 37 and 38: 75 cm by 90 cm; No. 39: 90 cm by 82 cm and No. 40: 82 cm by 90 cm

The Stations of the Cross (or the 'Way of the Cross' or 'Via Dolorosa') are the places where Jesus is believed to have halted on his way from Pilate's House to Golgotha for his crucifixion. In the late Middle Ages, under the influence of the Franciscans, the devotion of the 'Way of the Cross'

37

38

39

40

was introduced in the form of a series of stopping places for meditation or homilies, usually inside a church, but occasionally outside, each marked by a representation of the incident that was said to have taken place at that point. During Holy Week the priest and congregation of a Catholic or High Church Anglican parish may physically move round the Stations of the Cross day by day.

Originally there were seven 'stations' (based on the Gospel accounts of the 'Road to Calvary', for example, Luke 23: 26–32); later the number was doubled and fourteen remains the usual number today.

37 Number IV, *Jesus meets his blessed mother*
38 Number VII, *Jesus falls for the second time*
39 Number XIII, *The deposition (Jesus taken down from the cross)*
40 Number XIV, *The entombment (Jesus is laid in the sepulchre)*

See entry number 12 for Biblical text.
In Station Number XIII, showing the deposition, Jesus is taken down from the cross by Joseph of Arimathaea and Nicodemus. It is normal practice to show Joseph carrying the upper part of Jesus' body and Nicodemus the lower, so we may take it here that it is Joseph who has climbed the ladder and is controlling the linen winding sheet which is being used to control the weight of Jesus' body as it is lowered.

At the entombment (Station Number XIV) Jesus is shown laid on the ground, or in the sepulchre, with the three Marys. Traditionally one would identify the three figures as the Virgin Mary on the left, cradling Jesus' head, Mary Magdalene embracing his feet (interpreted as an act of penitence), while the third Mary is standing with her back to the viewer.

Roper produced two early sets of Stations of the Cross, one in 1959 for St Martin's Church, Roath, Cardiff and the other for St Saviour's Church, Splott, Cardiff in 1963. The four reliefs in the Methodist Collection are related to the St Saviour's Stations. In 1992 Roper explained, 'The Stations in the collection are replicas of the Stations at St Saviour's, Splott. They were modelled in clay and plaster moulds made of each. I destroyed ten moulds and kept the four which I liked best, it was from these four that I was able to make wax casts and proceed to the castings in metal.'

Roper stated in a letter in March 1963, 'I should want to mount these stations against an interesting timber background.' In St Martin's Church, Roath and St Saviour's Church, Splott the Stations are fixed directly to the wall, without even a delineating border. This results in their impact being reduced because they lose coherence and compactness as a result. The choice of the wood backing is very successful, both in the colour combination of the silver-grey aluminium against the golden-brown wood and because the wood provides a frame without over-emphasizing the border.

© *RW*

Georges Rouault

Born: Paris 1871
Died: Paris 1958

Studied: Ecole des Arts Décoratifs, Paris 1885; Ecole Nationale Supérieure des Beaux-Arts, Paris 1891–5

Selected commissions: stained glass windows for church at Plateau d'Assy, Haute Savoie, France 1945

Selected collections: Tate Gallery, London; Victoria and Albert Museum, London; Leeds University Collection

41 Aimez-vous les uns les autres (Love one another)
Aquatint from Miserere, 78 cm by 60 cm. Signed and dated bottom right corner 1923.

'I give you a new commandment, That you love one another. Just as I have loved you, you also should love one another. By this everyone will know that you are my disciples, if you have love for one another.'

(John 13: 34–35)

41

42

See also entry number 21 for Biblical text.

Jesus is shown on the cross with two standing figures on his left and a kneeling figure on his right. Jesus is naked except for a subligaculum (a thin cloth band around the waist and between the legs). His head is almost horizontal, lying along his right shoulder. The cross has a sign fixed to the top, with the letters 'INRI' (the initial letters of 'Iesus Nazarenus Rex Iudaeorum', the Roman text of the sign that John 19: 19–20 states was in three languages, Roman, Greek and Hebrew: 'Jesus of Nazareth King of the Jews'). There are two white buildings in the background. The cross runs out of the picture at the top and on each side and Jesus is a totally dominating figure.

The standing figures are not sufficiently delineated to allow us to identify them with certainty. It matters little: it is clear that the message is that we should love one another, whether it be St John looking after Mary, the mother of Jesus, or a more general commandment – a commission for all Christians and the Church.

42 Obéissant jusqu'à la mort et à la mort de la croix (Obedient to the point of death, even death on a cross)

Aquatint from Miserere, 76 cm by 60 cm. Signed and dated bottom right corner 1926.

Let the same mind be in you that was in Christ Jesus, who ... emptied himself, taking the form of a slave, being born in human likeness.
And being found in human form, he humbled himself, and became obedient to the point of death – even death on a cross.
(The Letter of Paul to the Philippians 2: 5–8)

Jesus is shown on the cross, from the waist up and with his arms extending out of the picture on each side. His head is surrounded by a vivid halo and his face is at peace, despite the agonies of crucifixion. The text of the print's title is strikingly portrayed.

Rouault's Miserere had a long and chequered history. The print and art dealer Ambroise Vollard was greatly struck by Rouault's work and initially suggested that he publish two books of Rouault's prints (with texts by André Suarès), one to be titled Miserere and the other Guerre (War). Rouault's first thoughts date from around 1913. He produced 100 India ink drawings (fifty for each volume) and delivered them to Vollard who, believing that Rouault's métier was painting rather than drawing, returned them, asking Rouault to re-do the drawings as paintings suitable for printmaking.

Rouault set about this task and delivered the 100 re-done paintings to Vollard who arranged for copper plates to be made from them. Instead of then proceeding to print them, Vollard decided that Rouault could improve them if he worked on the plates one by one, 'finishing' them by hand. Rouault therefore set to work, taking over five years and producing up to fifteen separate and distinguishable versions of some plates before he was satisfied. (Rouault was a perfectionist who was seldom totally satisfied with a work and kept reworking his paintings.)

One result of the reworking of the plates was that the number of prints fell from 100 to fifty-eight and, as he worked on the project, the separation into two books became increasingly irrelevant. A single edition of prints, Miserere, ensued which was divided into two parts, Miserere with thirty-three plates and Guerre with twenty-five plates. The Suarès text did not materialize. In 1927 Rouault personally supervised the printing of the plates and delivered the results (450 impressions of each plate) to Vollard, who decided that the time was not ripe to issue them and put them into store.

Knowledge of this mammoth project spread throughout the art-world in France and abroad, but the prints remained in store. They were still in store in 1939 when Vollard died and remained so throughout the Second World War. In 1948 Rouault published them. By then he was 77, having started work on the project when he was 42. (See Miserere, Le Société d'Edition l'Etoile filante, Paris 1948, and facsimile, Trianon Press, London 1950.)

One of the great French painters of the twentieth century, indeed one of the great painters, Rouault was a profoundly religious painter. Gustave Moreau, his teacher at the end of the nineteenth century, who believed that 'art can lead to religion, and to real religion, the kind that elevates the soul', commented of Rouault, 'art for you is serious, sober and in its essence, religious'. From the beginning Rouault painted religious subjects and he continued to do so throughout his life, alongside the paintings of clowns and prostitutes for which he is perhaps better known.

© **RW**

Jyoti Sahi

Born: 1944 Pune, India

Studied: Camberwell School of Arts and Crafts 1959-63

Selected collections: School of Divinity, University of Edinburgh; St Andrew's Church, Aylestone, Leicestershire

43 Dalit Madonna
Oil on canvas, c. 2002. 148 cm by 119 cm.

See entry number 19 for Biblical text.

Through his art, Jyoti Sahi has sought to illuminate Christianity with the faith and cultural traditions of India. In this painting, the image has arisen out of an important folk symbol, the grinding stone, which, often secured to the ground, is to be found in every traditional home. It consists of two parts. One is fixed and stable, and is known as the "Mother Stone". It generally has a hollow in its centre, into which fits a smaller seed or egg-shaped stone which is called the "Baby Stone". This is free to move about, and is used to grind various food stuffs which are placed in the hollow of the Mother Stone. There are a number of rites of passage involving the grinding stone. Thus at the time of marriage, the bride and groom are often made to stand on the stone, and are reminded that, as the grinding stone remains fixed and stable at the heart of the home, so also their love for each other should be immovable.

Relating the figure of Mary and her son Jesus to this symbol, one can draw attention to the way that the bond between mother and child is also linked to the preparation of daily bread and other items of food which are blended together in the grinding stone. This communion of love is the source of all plenty, and we can think of the relationship of Mary to Jesus when saying "Give us this day our daily bread".

The word "Dalit" means broken (it has been used in self-designation by those in South Asia who have been traditionally regarded as low caste or 'untouchable'). In a way, grain and other items of food are also broken in the grinding stone, but this breaking is preparatory to the creation of wholesome food for the family. As the early Father of the Church, Ignatius of Antioch said,'there can be no bread without a process of breaking and transforming'. In the relationship of Jesus to Mary there is suffering, but also, in their communion, a possibility of life and hope.

Jyoti Sahi's father was a Hindu, his mother a Christian, and it was his father who decided that he should be brought up as a Christian. A close family friend was an artist and Jyoti comments 'I can still remember the smell of paint which pervaded his studio. I was seven years old when I decided I would like to be an artist like him'.

Just after he had completed his Diploma in the UK, Jyoti Sahi was invited by Dom Bede Griffiths to join him in his newly founded ashram in South India. After teaching art for some years in India, he joined Fr. Bede and it was in this Ashram that he met his wife Jane, who is English, and from a Quaker background. They were married in 1970 and came to live in Bangalore where he was connected with the National Biblical, Catechetical and Liturgical Centre founded by the Catholic Bishops Conference of India, soon after the Second Vatican Council, to reflect on the relation of the Church in India to Indian Cultures and Spirituality. He is still linked to this centre, having founded an Art Ashram (The Indian School of Art for Peace) in a village outside Bangalore in 1984.

© T

F N Souza

Born: Goa, India 1924
Died: Mumbai, India 2002

Studied: Sir J J School of Art, Bombay 1940–45; Central School of Art, London

Selected collections: Tate Gallery, London; Victoria and Albert Museum, London

44 The crucifixion
Oil, 1962, 105 cm by 77 cm. Signed at the foot of the cross on the right, 'Souza 62'.

And it was now about noon, and darkness came over the whole land until three in the afternoon, while the sun's light failed.

(Luke 23: 44–45)

See also entry number 21 for Biblical text.

Jesus, clearly in great pain, hangs upon the cross with St John, in a grey cloak and trousers, on his right and a second figure, probably a woman, perhaps Mary the mother of Jesus,

43

44

standing, in a brown robe, on his left. Faint, ghostly echoes of the cross (and buildings) can just be made out in the background and the cross is topped by the INRI sign. While the figures are, as it were, well lit, the scene is set in darkness. The sun (or moon) appears in the sky on Jesus' left-hand side. Perhaps it is the moon imposed over the sun, the solar eclipse suggested in the Bible.

It was traditional to portray the sun and moon in crucifixions, these being pre-Christian symbols taken over by the Church. They represent the New and Old Testaments, with the sun usually being found on Jesus' right-hand side.

The painting is overtly expressionistic in style and the figure on Jesus' left (on the right as we look) is conveyed in a cubist style, with four superimposed eyes, two looking at Jesus and two looking out of the painting at the viewer.

F N Souza was born in Goa, the Portuguese enclave in west India where he was brought up as a Catholic. He went to a Jesuit high school in Bombay and in his teens thought of becoming a priest. God seemed a fearful person to him as a youth and 'God's servants went

around in dread and awe of him'.
In 1940 he went to the Western-orientated Sir J J School of Art in Bombay but was expelled in 1945 for political activity, joining the Communist Party in 1947. The same year he founded the Progressive Artists Group and won the major award in the Bombay Art Society exhibition. In the following year he was included in the exhibition of Indian Art at the Royal Academy in London. He moved to London in 1949.

His Catholic upbringing meant that he was always a religious painter and his Goan, Indian background, together with his own artistic development meant that he was always a full-blooded painter, producing 'rather bloody crucifixions' (see Dr Richard Taylor, Jesus in Indian Paintings, Christian Literature Society, Madras 1975, 2nd edition).

As Edwin Mullins says 'Souza's treatment of the figurative image is richly varied. Besides the violence, the eroticism and the satire, there is a religious quality about his work which is medieval in its simplicity and in its unsophisticated sense of wonder. Some of the most moving of Souza's paintings are those which convey a spirit of awe in the presence of divine power … in his religious work there is a quality of fearfulness and terrible grandeur which even Rouault and Graham Sutherland have not equalled in this century' (Edwin Mullins: F N Souza, Blond, London 1962).

© *RW*

Euryl Stevens

Born: Tonypandy, Rhondda Valley, Wales 1939

Studied: Birmingham College of Arts and Crafts 1957–61; Royal Academy Schools, London 1961–4

Selected collections: Worcester Art Gallery and Museum

45 The raising of Lazarus
Oil, 1964, 125 cm by 100 cm. Unsigned.

See entry number 32 for Biblical text.

The raising of Lazarus is painted symbolically rather than naturalistically, being set in modern times in a large open area of parkland. Lazarus is portrayed at the bottom of the painting in his tomb, and then in four images from right to left across the canvas above the lowest level, in progressive stages of resurrection, with the empty tomb on the left-hand side. From the third scene from the right, in which Lazarus is kneeling, he rises in a sequence of four small white-clad figures, before finally materializing, as it were, at ground level in a bright pink robe. In this way, the painting is divided into two, and the bright colours of earth are contrasted with the blackness of death. The arms of Jesus embrace the scene with a

blessing, breaking forward, as if from the position of the viewer (compare the similar device used by John Reilly in his quite different painting of The raising of Lazarus, entry number 32). The picture is personalized by the artist giving Lazarus the face of her father, who died during the Second World War.

The miracle is witnessed by a great crowd, breaking forward from the distant, rolling parkland through a gap in a screen of trees. The watching crowd are assembled in their serried ranks and rows and held back on the right (as we look) by a chain of policemen. One woman has broken through the cordon and stands in front of the policeman on the far right. To the left of the pink-robed Lazarus, the crowd is hemmed in by a line (or two or three lines) of small clergymen and priests, behind whom two women stand, as if giants. They are Mary and Martha and, like the figures of Lazarus and Jesus, are painted to a different scale. Behind them, smaller and smaller figures recede into the distance.

A particularly striking aspect of the painting is a series of animal-headed figures, including a cat, dog, donkey, lion, monkey and deer, ranging from a dog-headed man in the line of policemen at the front (immediately by the pink-robed Lazarus), to a group of three deer-headed figures well back in the crowd. Euryl Stevens has commented that these figures with animals' heads represent the non-

45

one can find "a celebration of life" in the most unexpected work.'

Euryl Stevens painted the The raising of Lazarus in 1964, while at, or very shortly after leaving, the Royal Academy School.

© *RW*

Graham Sutherland

Born: London 1903
Died: Menton, France 1980

Studied: Goldsmith's College, London 1921–6

Selected commissions:
Crucifixion, St Matthew's Church, Northampton 1944; Christ in Majesty (tapestry), Coventry Cathedral 1952; Noli Me Tangere, Chichester Cathedral 1960; Crucifixion, St Aidan's Church, East Acton, London 1960

Selected collections: Tate Gallery, London; National Portrait Gallery, London; Scottish National Gallery of Modern Art, Edinburgh; National Museum of Wales, Cardiff; Fitzwilliam Museum, Cambridge; Birmingham City Museum and Art Gallery

believers, people with no need for religion (like animals in the jungle) a category in which she would place herself. She wrote in 1992
'I ... can't remember a time when I ever believed. Creating is the nearest I ever get to religion. Seeing a good exhibition where painters have expressed their emotions and reactions to life in their world – I find very stimulating. Pictures portraying Mary and Jesus do nothing for me but

46 The deposition
Oil, 1947, 50 cm by 45 cm. Signed bottom right 'Sutherland'.

See entry numbers 12 and 21 for Biblical texts.

46

The figure of Jesus is conveyed schematically, almost abstractly, lying on a tomb, in front of the cross which stands in the centre of a gap in a lowish wall. Two strips of linen run in a gentle loop from the ends of the wall, either to, or behind, the cross.

Jesus' body forms a concave arc, lying unsupported on top of the lidless tomb, his legs resting on the tomb's edge on one side and his shoulders on the other. His head, which is totally abstracted in a semi-circular or semi-spherical form, falls back horizontally. A linen cloth is wrapped around his feet and falls in a wide, low loop under his body and is secured at the right-hand end under his left shoulder.

Graham Sutherland is perhaps the best-known twentieth-century British painter or creator of religious works. The Crucifixion at St Matthew's Church in Northampton in 1944–6 was followed by a version of the deposition (now in the Fitzwilliam Museum in Cambridge) in 1946; the Methodist deposition in 1947; the tapestry of Christ in Glory at Coventry Cathedral (1960); a Noli me tangere (1961) at Chichester Cathedral; and a further Crucifixion at St Aidan's Church at East Acton in West London (1963).

In 1962–3 Sutherland was approached to see if he would accept a commission for a religious painting. At the time, and for the next few years, he was unable to do so (he was busy with the East Acton Crucifixion, stained glass designs for a church in Ipswich, and portraits of The Queen Mother, Kenneth Clark and Konrad Adenaur) and so in 1964 John Gibbs took the opportunity to purchase The deposition at Sothebys and it was duly added to the Methodist Collection.

The painting has an interesting history. It was bought by Stephen Spender, who in turn gave it to his wife who sold it in 1962, probably to provide the down-payment for their house at Mas de St Jérôme in France. It comes from a transitional period in Sutherland's life – the progression from his early work to his mature style – and this placing, stylistically as well as chronologically, is borne out by Sutherland's comment in a letter to Douglas Wollen in 1964, 'I think you are quite right in thinking that it does not fully represent my work in the field. Though there are elements in it which I like.'

All his works from the late 1940s are influenced by photographs he saw of the victims of the Nazi concentration camps and by Picasso's recent work, as well as by Grunewald. In addition, it is perhaps not too fanciful to suggest that the clean, schematic lines of this painting, with the featureless face and the cool grey-blue colours, also represent a return to the influence of Sutherland's early experience as a railway engineering draughtsman at Derby and his continuing interest in machines, revealed in many of his war-time paintings. This deposition is certainly very different from the slightly earlier expressionist, violent, even grotesque version in the Fitzwilliam Museum.

The cool blues and greys of the painting are central to the effect it produces on the viewer – an unemotional, calm and detached effect – and represent a good example of Sutherland's claim (in an article in The Listener in 1951) that 'colour has two major functions. It is form and it is mood. That is to say that by its warmth or coldness, it can create form; it can also create a mood.'

One can also see a correlation between the flowing, curved lines and jagged, spiky edges and the thorns that were increasingly interesting Sutherland from 1946 onwards.

© *RW*

Sadao Watanabe

Born: Tokyo 1913
Died: Tokyo 1996

Studied: In the workshop of Serizawa, master of the stencil-dying technique

Selected collections: British Museum, London

47 Christ enters Jerusalem

Stencil: natural pigments and ink on paper, 1982, 99cm by 67cm
Print no 13 of 100

See entry number 1 for Biblical text.

This was a favourite theme with Watanabe with at least four other versions being known. In this version most of the important elements of the Biblical tradition are present, although the onlookers are phlegmatic rather than enthusiastic. Jesus, largely in green, is centre stage on the donkey riding over ground that is covered with palm branches, discarded robes and flower heads. Up in a spindly tree, there is a small man who must be Zacchaeus (see the comments on entry number 1).

Sadao Watanabe's father died when he was ten years old. He left school early and became an apprentice in a dyer's shop. He was introduced to Christianity by a neighbour and was baptized at the age of seventeen. After working for some years with a textile printer, designing Kimono fabrics, he came across Serizawa Keisuke, from whom he learnt the ancient Okinawan technique of stencil- dying using hand-made paper and natural pigments.

The paper for both the stencils and the prints was handmade from the inner bark of the paper mulberry tree. That used for printing was coated with a plant-based mucilage. When dry, it was crumpled and then flattened to give a characteristic appearance. Watanabe would place a cut stencil on a light box with a piece of the paper on top of it. Using the stencil as a guide, he painted on colours: traditional pigments in soybean milk. When the paints were dry, he put the cut stencil design on top of the printing paper, adjusted to the coloured areas, and then placed a fine silk screen over it. A rice paste was applied, after which both the silk screen and stencil were removed. After the paste had dried, he brushed black ink over the entire design. In the final stage, the paper was submerged in water and the paste gently brushed away, revealing the underlying colours.

In 1958 he began to make an impact in the USA by winning first

47

prize at the Modern Japanese Print Exhibition in New York City. His work soon became popular and was acquired by leading Museums. Despite his growing international reputation, Watanabe's main aim was to reach his fellow countrymen with the Christian message. Not only is his work executed in a traditional Japanese medium, but his Biblical themes are depicted in a Japanese setting. He liked his prints to hang in ordinary places where people gather, "because it was to them that Jesus brought the gospel". This, together with the use of natural material is characteristic of mingei : art for the people and by the people.

This work was given to the Trustees by a Roman Catholic priest Father Bruno, through the good offices of Rev The Lord Griffiths.

© *T*

About this publication

This booklet is the second edition of a publication that first appeared in 2000 and was reprinted in 2004. The text on the works falls into two categories. For those works present in the Collection in 2000, the entries come from the first edition of the 'Introduction'. They are edited versions of text that appears in Catalogue of the Methodist Church Collection of Modern Christian Art by Roger Wollen, published in 2003 by the Trustees of the Collection (ISBN 0-9538135-1-7, 178pp).This can be obtained from Methodist Publishing (www.mph.org.uk). The entries have been updated by the author. Entries on later acquisitions are written by a team of Trustees under the leadership of the Chairman, John Newton Gibbs.

Roger Wollen, the principal author, is the son of the Rev. Douglas Wollen who played such a key part in assembling the Methodist Collection. He has been involved in the arts for over forty years and now works as a freelance exhibition curator and lecturer in fine art based in Newcastle upon Tyne.

He has worked with the Barbican Art Gallery in London and the Hatton Gallery at Newcastle University on a major exhibition devoted to the artist and film-maker Derek Jarman, and with York City Art Gallery and Tullie House Museum and Art Gallery, Carlisle, on a touring show of contemporary Greek art, 'Greek Horizons'. Other exhibitions have been toured to venues in Tyne and Wear and projects in development include collaborations with the Centre for Life in Newcastle, Newcastle University, the Royal Botanical Gardens in Edinburgh and other venues in Britain and abroad.